For Victor with best wishes
from
Gisela Swanson.

Life—
How did it get here?
By evolution or by creation?

The numbers at the end of a sentence refer to the references at the end of this book.

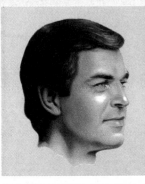

Millions of people today believe in evolution. Other millions believe in creation. Still others are uncertain what to believe. This book is for all such people. It presents a thoroughly researched examination of how life got here—and what this means for the future.

WATCH TOWER BIBLE AND TRACT SOCIETY OF PENNSYLVANIA
INTERNATIONAL BIBLE STUDENTS ASSOCIATION

Publishers
WATCHTOWER BIBLE AND TRACT SOCIETY OF NEW YORK, INC.
INTERNATIONAL BIBLE STUDENTS ASSOCIATION
Brooklyn, New York, U.S.A.

This Book Is Published in 16 Languages
Total Books Printed of All Editions
15,500,000 COPIES

Unless otherwise indicated, Scripture quotations are from the modern-language *New World Translation of the Holy Scriptures*, 1984 Edition

Life—How Did It Get Here? By Evolution or by Creation?   English (*ce-E*)   Made in the United States of America

Contents

Chapter 1

Life—How Did It Start?

LIFE is everywhere around us. It is evident in the humming of insects, the singing of birds, the rustlings of small animals in the underbrush. It exists in the icy polar regions and in parched deserts. It is present from the sea's sunlit surface to its darkest depths. High in the atmosphere tiny creatures float about. Beneath our feet untold trillions of microorganisms are at work in the soil, making it fertile for the growing of green plants, which sustain other forms of life.

Did life evolve or was it created?

2 Earth is packed with life so abundant and varied as to stagger the imagination. How did it all start? This planet of ours and all its inhabitants—how did they come to be here? More particularly, how did humankind get started? Did we evolve from apelike animals? Or were we created? Just how *did* we get here? And what does the answer imply for the future? Questions like these have been around for a long time and they are still unanswered in the minds of many.

---

1. How extensive is life on planet Earth?
2. What questions have long occupied many people's minds?

7

3 Perhaps you feel that these questions do not really affect you. You may think: 'It doesn't matter how I got here—I'm here. And I'll probably live for 60, 70 or maybe 80 years—who knows? But whether we were created or we evolved, it changes nothing for me now.' On the contrary, it could change a great deal—how long you live, the way you live, the conditions under which you live. How so? Because our entire attitude toward life and the future is influenced by our viewpoint on the origin of life. And how life came to be here will definitely affect the future course of history and our place in it.

Differing Viewpoints

4 In the view of many who accept the theory of evolution, life will always be made up of intense competition, with strife, hatred, wars and death. Some even feel that man may destroy himself in the near future. A prominent scientist stated: "We may have only another few decades until Doomsday. . . . the development of nuclear weapons and their delivery systems will, sooner or later, lead to global disaster."[1] Even if this did not happen soon, many believe that when a person's life span runs out in death he is then nonexistent forever. Others feel that, in the future, all life on earth will end. They theorize that the sun will expand into a red giant star, and as it does, "the oceans will boil, the atmosphere will evaporate away to space and a catastrophe of the most immense proportions imaginable will overtake our planet."[2]

5 Recoiling from these conclusions are the "scientific creationists." But their interpretation of the Genesis creation account has led them to claim that the earth is only 6,000 years old and that the six "days" allowed in Genesis for creation were each

Our entire attitude toward life and the future is influenced by our viewpoint on its origin

---

3. How do some feel about these questions, but why are they important to everyone?
4. How do many feel about the prospects for life on earth?
5. (a) How do the "scientific creationists" view the earth? (b) What questions does this viewpoint raise?

Only 6,000 years old?

only 24 hours long. But does such an idea accurately represent what the Bible is saying? Was the earth, and all its life forms, created in just six literal days? Or is there a reasonable alternative?

[6] In considering questions related to the origin of life, popular opinion or emotion sway many. To avoid this and to reach accurate conclusions, we need to consider the evidence with an open mind. It is interesting to note, too, that even evolution's best-known advocate, Charles Darwin, indicated an awareness of his theory's limitations. In his conclusion to *The Origin of Species,* he wrote of the grandeur of the "view of life, with its several powers, having been originally breathed by the Creator into a few forms or into one,"[3] thus making it evident that the subject of origins was open to further examination.

Science Not at Issue

[7] Before proceeding further, a clarification may be helpful: Scientific achievement is not at issue

---

6. On what should we base our conclusions about the origin of life on earth, and how did Darwin leave the subject open?
7. What clarification is made about science and our respect for it?

9

here. Every informed person is aware of the amazing accomplishments of scientists in many fields. Scientific study has dramatically increased our knowledge of the universe and of the earth and of living things. Studies of the human body have opened up improved ways of treating illnesses and injuries. Rapid advances in electronics have ushered in the computer age, which is altering our lives. Scientists have performed astounding feats, even sending men to the moon and back. It is only right to respect the skills that have added so greatly to our knowledge of the world around us, from minutely small things to infinitely large ones.

Those who accept evolution contend that creation is not scientific; but can it be fairly said that the theory of evolution itself is truly scientific?

[8] It may also be useful to clarify definitions at this point: *Evolution,* as used in this book, refers to organic evolution—the theory that the first living organism developed from nonliving matter. Then, as it reproduced, it is said to have changed into different kinds of living things, producing ultimately all forms of life that have ever existed on earth, including humans. And all of this is believed to have been accomplished without intelligent direction or supernatural intervention. *Creation,* on the other hand, is the conclusion that the appearing of living things can only be explained by the existence of an Almighty God who designed and made the universe and all the basic kinds of life upon the earth.

Some Vital Questions

[9] Obviously, there are profound differences between the theory of evolution and the Genesis creation account. Those who accept evolution contend that creation is not scientific. But in fairness, it could also be asked: Is evolution itself truly scientific? On the other hand, is Genesis just another

8. How is the term *evolution* used in this book, and to what does *creation* refer?
9. What do those who accept evolution contend about creation, but what questions may come to mind about both evolution and creation?

ancient creation myth, as many contend? Or is it in harmony with the discoveries of modern science? And what about other questions that trouble so many: If there is an all-powerful Creator, why is there so much war, famine and disease that send millions to an early grave? Why would he permit so much suffering? Also, if there is a Creator, does he reveal what the future will hold?

It is right to respect the scientific skills that have added so greatly to our knowledge

[10] It is the aim of this book to examine such questions and related issues. The publishers hope that you will consider its contents with an open mind. Why is this so important? Because this information could prove to be of greater value to you than you may yet realize.

---

10. (a) What is the aim of this book, and the publishers' hope? (b) Why is it so important to consider these matters?

Some Things to Think About

Our world is filled with so many marvelous things:

Big things: A setting sun that turns the western sky into a blaze of colors. A night sky, packed with stars. A forest of towering trees, run through by shafts of light. Jagged mountain ranges, their icy summits glistening in the sun. Surging, wind-tossed oceans. These things exhilarate us, fill us with awe.

Little things: A tiny bird, a warbler, flying high over the Atlantic, heading toward Africa on its way to South America. At some 20,000 feet it picks up a prevailing wind that turns it toward South America. Directed by its migrating instinct, it follows its course for several days and 2,400 miles—three quarters of an ounce of courage wrapped in feathers. We are filled with admiration and wonder.

Ingenious things: Bats that use sonar. Eels that make electricity. Gulls that desalt seawater. Wasps that make paper. Termites that install air conditioners. Octopuses that travel by jet propulsion. Birds that do weaving or build apartment houses. Ants that do gardening or sewing, or keep livestock. Fireflies with built-in flashlights. We marvel at such ingenuity.

Simple things: As life nears its end, it is the small things that we often focus upon, things that we had so often taken for granted: A smile. The touch of a hand. A kind word. A tiny flower. The singing of a bird. The warmth of the sun.

When we think about such big things that are breathtaking, little things that stir our admiration, ingenious things that fascinate us, simple things belatedly appreciated —to what do we attribute them? Just how can such things be explained? Where did they come from?

When a special centennial edition of Darwin's *Origin of Species* was to be published, W. R. Thompson, then director of the Commonwealth Institute of Biological Control, in Ottawa, Canada, was invited to write its introduction. In it he said: "As we know, there is a great divergence of opinion among biologists, not only about the causes of evolution but even about the actual process. This divergence exists because the evidence is unsatisfactory and does not permit any certain conclusion. It is therefore right and proper to draw the attention of the non-scientific public to the disagreements about evolution"[a]

Chapter 2

Disagreements About Evolution—Why?

THOSE who support the theory of evolution feel that it is now an established fact. They believe that evolution is an "actual occurrence," a "reality," a "truth," as one dictionary defines the word "fact." But is it?

[2] To illustrate: It was once believed that the earth was flat. Now it has been established for a certainty that it is spherical in shape. That is a fact. It was once believed that the earth was the center of the universe and that the heavens revolved around the earth. Now we know for sure that the earth revolves in an orbit around the sun. This, too, is a fact. Many things that were once only debated theories have been established by the evidence as solid fact, reality, truth.

"Darwinism, after a century and a quarter, is in a surprising amount of trouble"

1, 2. (a) How has the word "fact" been defined? (b) What are some examples of facts?

3 Would an investigation of the evidence for evolution leave one on the same solid ground? Interestingly, ever since Charles Darwin's book *The Origin of Species* was published in 1859, various aspects of the theory have been a matter of considerable disagreement even among top evolutionary scientists. Today, that dispute is more intense than ever. And it is enlightening to consider what advocates of evolution themselves are saying about the matter.

Evolution Under Assault

Questions below.

4 The scientific magazine *Discover* put the situation this way: "Evolution . . . is not only under attack by fundamentalist Christians, but is also being questioned by reputable scientists. Among paleontologists, scientists who study the fossil record, there is growing dissent from the prevailing view of Darwinism."[1] Francis Hitching, an evolutionist and author of the book *The Neck of the Giraffe,* stated: "For all its acceptance in the scientific world as the great unifying principle of biology, Darwinism, after a century and a quarter, is in a surprising amount of trouble."[2] *References.*

5 After an important conference of some 150 specialists in evolution held in Chicago, Illinois, a report concluded: "[Evolution] is undergoing its broadest and deepest revolution in nearly 50 years. . . . Exactly how evolution happened is now a matter of great controversy among biologists. . . . No clear resolution of the controversies was in sight."[3]

6 Paleontologist Niles Eldredge, a prominent evolutionist, said: "The doubt that has infiltrated the previous, smugly confident certitude of evolutionary biology's last twenty years has inflamed passions." He spoke of the "lack of total agreement

"Exactly how evolution happened is now a matter of great controversy among biologists"

---

3. (a) What indicates that evolution as an established "fact" is still in question? (b) What approach will be helpful in examining the current status of evolution?
4-6. What has been happening among those who promote evolution?

Of Darwin's book *The Origin of Species,* a London *Times* writer who accepts evolution wrote: "We have here the supreme irony that a book which has become famous for explaining the origin of species in fact does nothing of the kind"

even within the warring camps," and added, "things really are in an uproar these days . . . Sometimes it seems as though there are as many variations on each [evolutionary] theme as there are individual biologists."[4]

[7] A London *Times* writer, Christopher Booker (who accepts evolution), said this about it: "It was a beautifully simple and attractive theory. The only trouble was that, as Darwin was himself at least partly aware, it was full of colossal holes." Regarding Darwin's *Origin of Species,* he observed: "We have here the supreme irony that a book which has become famous for explaining the origin of species *in fact does nothing of the kind."*—Italics added.

[8] Booker also stated: "A century after Darwin's death, we still have not the slightest demonstrable or even plausible idea of how evolution really took place—and in recent years this has led to an extraordinary series of battles over the whole question. . . . a state of almost open war exists among the evolutionists themselves, with every kind of [evolutionary] sect urging some new modification." He concluded: "As to how and why it really happened, we have not the slightest idea and probably never shall."[5]

[9] Evolutionist Hitching agreed, saying: "Feuds concerning the theory of evolution exploded . . . Entrenched positions, for and against, were established in high places, and insults lobbed like mortar bombs from either side." He said that it is an academic dispute of far-reaching proportions, "po-

7, 8. How did one respected writer comment on Darwin's *Origin of Species?*
9. How is the situation among evolutionists in recent times described?

16

tentially one of those times in science when, quite suddenly, a long-held idea is overthrown by the weight of contrary evidence and a new one takes its place."[6] And Britain's *New Scientist* observed that "an increasing number of scientists, most particularly a growing number of evolutionists . . . argue that Darwinian evolutionary theory is no genuine scientific theory at all. . . . Many of the critics have the highest intellectual credentials."[7]

Dilemmas Over Origins

[10] Regarding the question of how life originated, astronomer Robert Jastrow said: "To their chagrin [scientists] have no clear-cut answer, because chemists have never succeeded in reproducing nature's experiments on the creation of life out of nonliving matter. Scientists do not know how that happened." He added: "Scientists have no proof that life was not the result of an act of creation."[8]

[11] But the difficulty does not stop with the origin of life. Consider such body organs as the eye, the ear, the brain. All are staggering in their complex-

---

10. Has an evolutionary origin of life on earth been established as fact?
11. Complex body organs present what difficulty for evolution?

ity, far more so than the most intricate man-made device. A problem for evolution has been the fact that all parts of such organs have to work together for sight, hearing or thinking to take place. Such organs would have been useless until all the individual parts were completed. So the question arises: Could the undirected element of chance that is thought to be a driving force of evolution have brought all these parts together at the right time to produce such elaborate mechanisms?

[12] Darwin acknowledged this as a problem. For example, he wrote: "To suppose that the eye . . . could have been formed by [evolution], seems, I freely confess, absurd in the highest degree."[9] More than a century has passed since then. Has the problem been solved? No. On the contrary, since Darwin's time what has been learned about the eye shows that it is even more complex than he understood it to be. Thus Jastrow said: "The eye appears to have been designed; no designer of telescopes could have done better."[10]

"The eye appears to have been designed; no designer of telescopes could have done better"

[13] If this is so of the eye, what, then, of the human brain? Since even a simple machine does not evolve by chance, how can it be a fact that the

---

12. (a) How did Darwin comment on the origin of the eye? (b) Is the problem nearer to being solved today?
13. What did one scientist conclude about the brain?

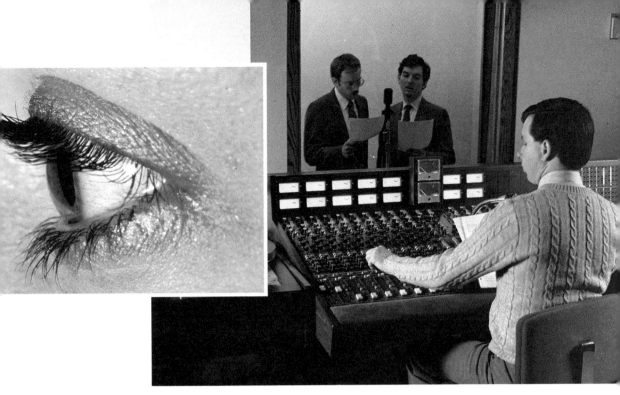

Said astronomer Robert Jastrow: "It is hard to accept the evolution of the human eye as a product of chance; it is even harder to accept the evolution of human intelligence as the product of random disruptions in the brain cells of our ancestors"

infinitely more complex brain did? Jastrow concluded: "It is hard to accept the evolution of the human eye as a product of chance; it is even harder to accept the evolution of human intelligence as the product of random disruptions in the brain cells of our ancestors."[11]

Dilemmas Over Fossils

[14] Millions of bones and other evidence of past life have been unearthed by scientists, and these are called fossils. If evolution were a fact, surely in all of this there should be ample evidence of one kind of living thing evolving into another kind. But the *Bulletin* of Chicago's Field Museum of Natural History commented: "Darwin's theory of [evolution] has always been closely linked to evidence from fossils, and probably most people assume that fos-

---

14. Is it true that the fossil evidence supports evolution?

19

Eohippus

Archaeopteryx

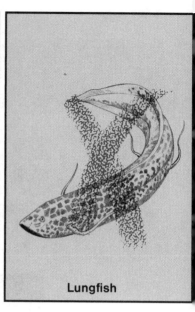

Lungfish

"Some of the classic cases of darwinian change in the fossil record . . . have had to be discarded or modified as a result of more detailed information."[c]—David Raup, Chicago's Field Museum of Natural History

sils provide a very important part of the general argument that is made in favor of darwinian interpretations of the history of life. Unfortunately, this is not strictly true."

[15] Why not? The *Bulletin* went on to say that Darwin "was embarrassed by the fossil record because it didn't look the way he predicted it would . . . the geologic record did not then and still does not yield a finely graduated chain of slow and progressive evolution." In fact now, after more than a century of collecting fossils, "we have even fewer examples of evolutionary transition than we had in Darwin's time," explained the *Bulletin*.[12] Why is this the case? Because the more abundant fossil evidence available today shows that some of the examples that were once used to support evolution now are seen not to do so at all.

[16] This failure of the fossil evidence to support

15. (a) How did Darwin view the fossil evidence in his day? (b) After more than a century of collecting fossils, what does the evidence reveal?
16. What do many evolutionary scientists now acknowledge?

gradual evolution has disturbed many evolutionists. In *The New Evolutionary Timetable,* Steven Stanley spoke of "the general failure of the record to display gradual transitions from one major group to another." He said: "The known fossil record is not, and never has been, in accord with [slow evolution]."[13] Niles Eldredge also admitted: "The pattern that we were told to find for the last 120 years does not exist."[14]

"The pattern that we were told to find for the last 120 years does not exist"

Newer Theories

[17] All of this has led many scientists to champion novel theories for evolution. *Science Digest* put it this way: "Some scientists are proposing even more rapid evolutionary changes and are now dealing quite seriously with ideas once popularized only in fiction."[15]

[18] For instance, some scientists have concluded that life could not have arisen spontaneously on earth. Instead, they speculate that it must have originated in outer space and then floated down to the earth. But that just pushes the problem of the origin of life further back and into a more forbidding setting. The perils confronting life in the hostile environment of outer space are well known. Is it likely, then, that life began *spontaneously* elsewhere in the universe and survived under such harsh conditions to reach the earth, and later to develop into life as we know it?

"Some scientists are proposing . . . [evolutionary] ideas once popularized only in fiction"

[19] Since the fossil record does not show a gradual development of life from one type into another, some evolutionists theorize that the process must have happened by jerks and starts, not at a steady pace. As *The World Book Encyclopedia* explains: "Many biologists think new species may be produced by sudden, drastic changes in genes."[16]

17. How did *Science Digest* comment on the newer theories?
18. What difficulty is there with the more recent theory that life began in outer space?
19, 20. What new theory are some evolutionists promoting?

While the fittest may *survive*, this does not explain how they *arrive*

20 Some adherents to this theory have called the process "punctuated equilibrium." That is, species maintain their "equilibrium" (they stay much the same), but every once in a while there is a "punctuation" (a big jump to evolve into something else). This is just the opposite of the theory that has been accepted by nearly all evolutionists for many decades. The gulf between the two theories was illustrated by a headline in *The New York Times:* "Theory of Rapid Evolution Attacked." The article noted that the newer "punctuated equilibrium" idea had "aroused new opposition" among those who hold to the traditional view.[17]

New theories contradict what has been accepted for many decades

21 Regardless of which theory is held, it is reasonable that there should be at least some evidence to show that one kind of life turns into another kind. But the gaps between different types of life found in the fossil record, as well as the gaps between different types of living things on earth today, still persist.

22 Also, it is revealing to see what has happened

21. (a) Regardless of which theory of evolution is accepted, what evidence should exist? (b) Yet what do the facts show?
22, 23. How has Darwin's idea of "survival of the fittest" been challenged in recent times?

to Darwin's long-accepted idea regarding the "survival of the fittest." This he called "natural selection." That is, he believed that nature "selected" the fittest living things to survive. As these "fit" ones supposedly acquired new features that worked to their advantage, they slowly evolved. But the evidence of the past 125 years shows that, while the fittest may indeed *survive,* this does not explain how they *arrived.* One lion may be fitter than another lion, but that does not explain how he got to be a lion. And all of his offspring will still be lions, not something else.

[23] Thus, in *Harper's* magazine, writer Tom Bethell commented: "Darwin made a mistake sufficiently serious to undermine his theory. And that mistake has only recently been recognized as such. . . . One organism may indeed be 'fitter' than another . . . This, of course, is not something which helps *create* the organism, . . . It is clear, I think, that there was something very, very wrong with such an idea." Bethell added: "As I see it the conclusion is pretty staggering: Darwin's theory, I believe, is on the verge of collapse."[18]

"Darwin's theory,
I believe, is on the verge
of collapse"

Fact or Theory?

[24] Summarizing some of the unsolved problems confronting evolution, Francis Hitching observed: "In three crucial areas where [the modern evolution theory] can be tested, it has failed: The *fossil record* reveals a pattern of evolutionary leaps rather than gradual change. *Genes* are a powerful stabilizing mechanism whose main function is to prevent new forms evolving. Random step-by-step *mutations* at the molecular level cannot explain the organized and growing complexity of life."—Italics added.

24, 25. (a) What are some of the areas in which evolution has not met the standard of being an established fact? (b) In line with what an evolutionist said about the modern theory, how could it be regarded?

25 Then Hitching concluded by making this observation: "To put it at its mildest, one may question an evolutionary theory so beset by doubts among even those who teach it. If Darwinism is truly the great unifying principle of biology, it encompasses extraordinarily large areas of ignorance. It fails to explain some of the most basic questions of all: how lifeless chemicals came alive, what rules of grammar lie behind the genetic code, how genes shape the form of living things." In fact, Hitching stated that he considered the modern theory of evolution "so inadequate that it deserves to be treated as a matter of faith."[19]

26 However, many advocates of evolution feel that they do have sufficient reason to insist that evolution is a fact. They explain that they are just arguing over details. But if any other theory had such enormous remaining difficulties, and such major contradictions among those who advocate it, would it so readily be pronounced a fact? Merely repeating that something is a fact does not make it a fact. As John R. Durant, a biologist, wrote in *The Guardian* of London: "Many scientists succumb to the temptation to be dogmatic, . . . over and over again the question of the origin of the species has been presented as if it were finally settled. Nothing could be further from the truth. . . . But the tendency to be dogmatic persists, and it does no service to the cause of science."[20]

"Over and over again the question of the origin of the species has been presented as if it were finally settled. Nothing could be further from the truth"

27 On the other hand, what about creation as an explanation for how life got here? Does it offer a framework for the evidence that is any more sound than the assertions that often underpin evolution? And, as the best-known creation account, does Genesis shed any credible light on how the earth and living things got here?

---

26. Why is it not reasonable to continue insisting that evolution is a fact?
27. What other framework for the evidence is there, which offers a basis for understanding how life got here?

24

Chapter 3

What Does Genesis Say?

AS WITH other things that are misrepresented or misunderstood, the first chapter of the Bible deserves at least a fair hearing. The need is to investigate and determine whether it harmonizes with known facts, not to mold it to fit some theoretical framework. Also to be remembered, the Genesis account was not written to show the "how" of creation. Rather, it covers major events in a progressive way, describing what things were formed, the order in which they were formed and the time interval, or "day," in which each first appeared.

2 When examining the Genesis account, it is helpful to keep in mind that it approaches matters from the standpoint of people on earth. So it describes events as they would have been seen by human observers had they been present. This can be noted from its treatment of events on the fourth Genesis "day." There the sun and moon are described as great luminaries in comparison to the stars. Yet many stars are far greater than our sun, and the moon is insignificant in comparison to them. But not to an earthly observer. So, as seen from the earth, the sun appears to be a 'greater light that rules the day' and the moon a 'lesser light that dominates the night.'—Genesis 1:14-18.

The Genesis account is given from the standpoint of an observer on earth

1. (a) What is the purpose of this discussion on Genesis, and what should be remembered? (b) How are events covered in the first chapter of Genesis?
2. (a) From whose standpoint are the Genesis events described? (b) How does the description of the luminaries indicate this?

3 The first part of Genesis indicates that the earth could have existed for billions of years before the first Genesis "day," though it does not say for how long. However, it does describe what earth's condition was just before that first "day" began: "Now the earth proved to be formless and waste and there was darkness upon the surface of the watery deep; and God's active force was moving to and fro over the surface of the waters."—Genesis 1:2.

How Long Is a Genesis "Day"?

4 Many consider the word "day" used in Genesis chapter 1 to mean 24 hours. However, in Genesis 1:5 God himself is said to divide day into a smaller period of time, calling just the light portion "day." In Genesis 2:4 *all* the creative periods are called *one "day"*: "This is a history of the heavens and the earth in the time of their being created, in the *day* [all six creative periods] that Jehovah God made earth and heaven."

5 The Hebrew word *yohm*, translated "day," can mean different lengths of time. Among the meanings possible, William Wilson's *Old Testament Word Studies* includes the following: "A day; it is frequently put for time in general, or for a long time; a whole period under consideration . . . Day is also put for a particular season or time when any extraordinary event happens."[1] This last sentence appears to fit the creative "days," for certainly they were periods when extraordinary events were described as happening. It also allows for periods much longer than 24 hours.

6 Genesis chapter 1 uses the expressions "evening" and "morning" relative to the creative peri-

---

3. How is the earth described before the first "day"?
4. What indication is there in the creation account itself that the word "day" does not mean just a 24-hour period?
5. What is one meaning of the Hebrew word for "day" that indicates longer periods can be understood?
6. Why does the use of "evening" and "morning" not necessarily limit a "day" to 24 hours?

ods. Does this not indicate that they were 24 hours long? Not necessarily. In some places people often refer to a man's lifetime as his "day." They speak of "my father's day" or "in Shakespeare's day." They may divide up that lifetime "day," saying "in the morning [or dawn] of his life" or "in the evening [or twilight] of his life." So 'evening and morning' in Genesis chapter 1 does not limit the meaning to a literal 24 hours.

[7] "Day" as used in the Bible can include summer and winter, the passing of seasons. (Zechariah 14:8) "The day of harvest" involves many days. (Compare Proverbs 25:13 and Genesis 30:14.) A thousand years are likened to a day. (Psalm 90:4; 2 Peter 3: 8, 10) "Judgment Day" covers many years. (Matthew 10:15; 11:22-24) It would seem reasonable that the "days" of Genesis could likewise have embraced long periods of time—millenniums. What, then, took place during those creative eras? Is the Bible's account of them scientific? Following is a review of these "days" as expressed in Genesis.

Day 1: "Let light come to be"

First "Day"

[8] "'Let light come to be.' Then there came to be light. And God began calling the light Day, but the darkness he called Night. And there came to be evening and there came to be morning, a first day." —Genesis 1:3, 5.

[9] Of course the sun and moon were in outer space long before this first "day," but their light did not reach the surface of the earth for an earthly observer to see. Now, light evidently came to be visible on earth on this first "day," and the rotating earth began to have alternating days and nights.

[10] Apparently, the light came in a gradual pro-

---

7. What other uses show "day" could be more than 24 hours?
8, 9. What came to be on the first "day," and is Genesis saying that the sun and moon were created at that time?
10. In what way could this light have come, and what kind of light is indicated?

Day 2: "Let an expanse come to be"

cess, extending over a long period of time, not instantaneously as when you turn on an electric light bulb. The Genesis rendering by translator J. W. Watts reflects this when it says: "And gradually light came into existence." (*A Distinctive Translation of Genesis*) This light was from the sun, but the sun itself could not be seen through the overcast. Hence, the light that reached earth was "light diffused," as indicated by a comment about verse 3 in Rotherham's *Emphasised Bible.*—See footnote *b* for verse 14.

Second "Day"

[11] "'Let an expanse come to be in between the waters and let a dividing occur between the waters and the waters.' Then God proceeded to make the expanse and to make a division between the waters that should be beneath the expanse and the waters that should be above the expanse. And it came to be so. And God began to call the expanse Heaven."—Genesis 1:6-8.

[12] Some translations use the word "firmament" instead of "expanse." From this the argument is made that the Genesis account borrowed from creation myths that represent this "firmament" as a metal dome. But even the King James Version Bible, which uses "firmament," says in the margin, "expansion." This is because the Hebrew word *ra·qi′a‛,* translated "expanse," means to stretch out or spread out or expand.

[13] The Genesis account says that God did it, but it does not say how. In whatever way the described separation occurred, it would look as though the 'waters above' had been pushed up from the earth. And birds could later be said to fly in "the expanse of the heavens," as stated at Genesis 1:20.

11, 12. (a) What is described for the second "day"? (b) How has the Hebrew word for this development sometimes been mistranslated, and what does it really mean?
13. The expanse may have looked as though what had happened?

28

Third "Day"

[14] "'Let the waters under the heavens be brought together into one place and let the dry land appear.' And it came to be so. And God began calling the dry land Earth, but the bringing together of the waters he called Seas." (Genesis 1:9, 10) As usual, the account does not describe how this was done. No doubt, tremendous earth movements would have been involved in the formation of land areas. Geologists would explain such major upheavals as catastrophism. But Genesis indicates direction and control by a Creator.

[15] In the Biblical account where God is described as questioning Job about his knowledge of the earth, a variety of developments concerning earth's history are described: its measurements, its cloud masses, its seas and how their waves were limited by dry land—many things in general about the creation, spanning long periods of time. Among these things, comparing earth to a building, the Bible says that God asked Job: "Into what have its socket pedestals been sunk down, or who laid its cornerstone?"—Job 38:6.

Day 3: "Let the dry land appear"

---

14. How is the third "day" described?
15, 16. (a) What points were raised to Job about the earth? (b) How deep do the roots of continents and mountains go, and what is likened to a "cornerstone" for earth?

Day 3: "Let the earth cause grass to shoot forth"

[16] Interestingly, like "socket pedestals," earth's crust is much thicker under continents and even more so under mountain ranges, pushing deep into the underlying mantle, like tree roots into soil. "The idea that mountains and continents had roots has been tested over and over again, and shown to be valid," says *Putnam's Geology*.[2] Oceanic crust is only about 5 miles thick, but continental roots go down about 20 miles and mountain roots penetrate about twice that far. And all earth's layers press inward upon earth's core from all directions, making it like a great "cornerstone" of support.

[17] Whatever means were used to accomplish the raising up of dry land, the important point is: Both the Bible and science recognize it as one of the stages in the forming of the earth.

Land Plants on Third "Day"

[18] The Bible account adds: "'Let the earth cause grass to shoot forth, vegetation bearing seed, fruit trees yielding fruit according to their kinds, the seed of which is in it, upon the earth.' And it came to be so."—Genesis 1:11.

---

17. What is important relative to the appearance of dry land?
18, 19. (a) In addition to dry land, what else appeared on the third "day"? (b) What does the Genesis account not do?

¹⁹ Thus by the close of this third creative period, three broad categories of land plants had been created. The diffused light would have become quite strong by then, ample for the process of photosynthesis so vital to green plants. Incidentally, the account here does not mention every "kind" of plant that came on the scene. Microscopic organisms, water plants and others are not specifically named, but likely were created on this "day."

Fourth "Day"

²⁰ "'Let luminaries come to be in the expanse of the heavens to make a division between the day and the night; and they must serve as signs and for seasons and for days and years. And they must serve as luminaries in the expanse of the heavens to shine upon the earth.' And it came to be so. And God proceeded to make the two great luminaries, the greater luminary for dominating the day and the lesser luminary for dominating the night, and also the stars."—Genesis 1:14-16.

²¹ Previously, on the first "day," the expression "Let light come to be" was used. The Hebrew word there used for "light" is *'ohr,* meaning light in a general sense. But on the fourth "day," the Hebrew word changes to *ma·'ohr',* which means the source of the light. Rotherham, in a footnote on "Luminaries" in the *Emphasised Bible,* says: "In ver. 3, *'ôr* [*'ohr*], light diffused." Then he goes on to show that the Hebrew word *ma·'ohr'* in verse 14 means something "affording light." On the first "day" diffused light evidently penetrated the swaddling bands, but the sources of that light could not have been seen by an earthly observer because of the cloud layers still enveloping the earth. Now, on this fourth "day," things apparently changed.

---

20. What divisions in time became possible by the appearance of the luminaries in the expanse?
21. How did the light of the fourth "day" differ from that of the first?

31

Day 4: 'Let luminaries come to be in the expanse, the greater for dominating the day and the lesser for dominating the night'

[22] An atmosphere initially rich in carbon dioxide may have caused an earth-wide hot climate. But the lush growth of vegetation during the third and fourth creative periods would absorb some of this heat-retaining blanket of carbon dioxide. The vegetation, in turn, would release oxygen—a requirement for animal life.—Psalm 136:7-9.

[23] Now, had there been an earthly observer, he would be able to discern the sun, moon and stars, which would "serve as signs and for seasons and for days and years." (Genesis 1:14) The moon would indicate the passing of lunar months, and the sun the passing of solar years. The seasons that now "came to be" on this fourth "day" would no doubt have been much milder than they became later on. —Genesis 1:15; 8:20-22.

Fifth "Day"

[24] "'Let the waters swarm forth a swarm of living souls and let flying creatures fly over the earth upon the face of the expanse of the heavens.' And God proceeded to create the great sea monsters and every living soul that moves about, which the waters swarmed forth according to their kinds, and every winged flying creature according to its kind." —Genesis 1:20, 21.

[25] It is of interest to note that the nonhuman creatures with which the waters were to swarm are called "living souls." This term would also apply to the "flying creatures [that] fly over the earth upon the face of the expanse." And it would also embrace the forms of sea and air life, such as the sea monsters, whose fossil remains scientists have found in recent times.

Day 5: 'Let the waters swarm forth living souls and let flying creatures fly over the earth'

---

22. What development on the fourth "day" could have contributed to the coming of animal life?
23. What major changes are described for this time?
24. What kinds of creatures were said to appear on the fifth "day," and within what limits would they reproduce?
25. What were the creatures that appeared on the fifth "day" called?

Sixth "Day"

26 "'Let the earth put forth living souls according to their kinds, domestic animal and moving animal and wild beast of the earth according to its kind.' And it came to be so."—Genesis 1:24.

27 Thus on the sixth "day," land animals characterized as wild and domestic appeared. But this final "day" was not over. One last remarkable "kind" was to come:

28 "And God went on to say: 'Let us make man in our image, according to our likeness, and let them have in subjection the fish of the sea and the flying creatures of the heavens and the domestic animals and all the earth and every moving animal that is moving upon the earth.' And God proceeded to create the man in his image, in God's image he

Day 6: 'Domestic animal and wild beast according to its kind'

26-28. What took place on the sixth "day," and what was remarkable about the last act of creation?

Day 6: "Male and female he created them"

created him; male and female he created them."
—Genesis 1:26, 27.

[29] Chapter 2 of Genesis apparently adds some details. However, it is not, as some have concluded, another account of creation in conflict with that of chapter 1. It just takes up at a point in the third "day," after dry land appeared but before land plants were created, adding details that were pertinent to the arrival of humans—Adam the living soul, his garden home, Eden, and the woman Eve, his wife.—Genesis 2:5-9, 15-18, 21, 22.

[30] The foregoing is presented to help us understand what Genesis says. And this quite realistic account indicates that the creative process continued throughout a period of, not just 144 hours (6 × 24), but over many millenniums of time.

How Did Genesis Know?

[31] Many find it hard to accept this creation ac-

29, 30. How can the variance between Genesis chapter 2 and chapter 1 be understood?
31. (a) How do some misrepresent the Genesis account? (b) What shows their contentions to be inaccurate?

count. They contend that it is drawn from the creation myths of ancient peoples, primarily those from ancient Babylon. However, as one recent Bible dictionary noted: "No myth has yet been found which explicitly refers to the creation of the universe" and the myths "are marked by polytheism and the struggles of deities for supremacy in marked contrast to the Heb[rew] monotheism of [Genesis] 1-2."[3] Regarding Babylonian creation legends, the trustees of the British Museum stated: "The fundamental conceptions of the Babylonian and Hebrew accounts are essentially different."[4]

[32] From what we have considered, the Genesis creation account emerges as a scientifically sound document. It reveals the larger categories of plants and animals, with their many varieties, reproducing

---

32. How has the creation account in Genesis been shown to be scientifically sound?

The Babylonian creation myth that is claimed by some to be a basis for the Genesis creation account:

The god Apsu and the goddess Tiamat made other gods.

Later Apsu became distressed with these gods and tried to kill them, but instead he was killed by the god Ea.

Tiamat sought revenge and tried to kill Ea, but instead she was killed by Ea's son Marduk.

Marduk split her body in half, and from one half he made the sky and from the other half he made the earth.

Then Marduk, with Ea's aid, made mankind from the blood of another god, Kingu.[a]

Does it seem to you that this type of tale bears any similarity to the Genesis creation narrative?

35

only "according to their kinds." The fossil record provides confirmation of this. In fact, it indicates that each "kind" appeared suddenly, with no true transitional forms linking it with any previous "kind," as required by the evolution theory.

The fossil record confirms reproduction only "according to their kinds"

[33] All the knowledge of the wise men of Egypt could not have furnished Moses, the writer of Genesis, any clue to the process of creation. The creation myths of ancient peoples bore no resemblance to what Moses wrote in Genesis. Where, then, did Moses learn all these things? Apparently from someone who was there.

[34] The science of mathematical probability offers striking proof that the Genesis creation account

33. Where only could the information in the Genesis creation account have come from?
34. What other line of evidence underlines the soundness of the Genesis outline of events?

A well-known geologist said this about the Genesis creation account:

"If I as a geologist were called upon to explain briefly our modern ideas of the origin of the earth and the development of life on it to a simple, pastoral people, such as the tribes to whom the Book of Genesis was addressed, I could hardly do better than follow rather closely much of the language of the first chapter of Genesis."[b] This geologist, Wallace Pratt, also noted that the order of events—from the origin of the oceans, to the emergence of land, to the appearance of marine life, and then to birds and mammals—is essentially the sequence of the principal divisions of geologic time.

must have come from a source with knowledge of the events. The account lists 10 major stages in this order: (1) a beginning; (2) a primitive earth in darkness and enshrouded in heavy gases and water; (3) light; (4) an expanse or atmosphere; (5) large areas of dry land; (6) land plants; (7) sun, moon and stars discernible in the expanse, and seasons beginning; (8) sea monsters and flying creatures; (9) wild and tame beasts, mammals; (10) man. Science agrees that these stages occurred in this general order. What are the chances that the writer of Genesis just guessed this order? The same as if you picked at random the numbers 1 to 10 from a box, and drew them in consecutive order. The chances of doing this *on your first try* are 1 in 3,628,800! So, to say the writer just happened to list the foregoing events in the right order without getting the facts from somewhere is not realistic.

The chances of doing this on the first try are 1 in 3,628,800

[35] However, evolutionary theory does not allow for a Creator who was there, knew the facts and could reveal them to humans. Instead, it attributes the appearance of life on earth to the spontaneous generation of living organisms from inanimate chemicals. But could undirected chemical reactions relying on mere chance create life? Are scientists themselves convinced that this could happen? Please see the next chapter.

---

35. What questions are raised, and where are the answers to be discussed?

Chapter 4

Could Life Originate by Chance?

WHEN Charles Darwin advanced his theory of evolution he conceded that life may have been "originally breathed by the Creator into a few forms or into one."[1] But present-day evolutionary theory generally eliminates any mention of a Creator. Instead, the theory of the spontaneous generation of life, once repudiated, has been revived in a somewhat altered form.

[2] Belief in a form of spontaneous generation can be traced back for centuries. In the 17th century C.E., even respected men of science, including Francis Bacon and William Harvey, accepted the theory. However, by the 19th century Louis Pasteur and other scientists had seemingly dealt it a deathblow, having proved by experiments that life comes only from previous life. Nevertheless, out of necessity, evolutionary theory assumes that long ago microscopic life must somehow have arisen spontaneously from nonliving matter.

A New Form of Spontaneous Generation

[3] A current evolutionary position on life's starting point is summarized in his book, *The Selfish Gene*, by Richard Dawkins. He speculates that in the

---

1. (a) What did Charles Darwin concede about the origin of life? (b) What idea has present-day evolutionary theory revived?
2. (a) What previous belief involving spontaneous generation was proved false? (b) Though admitting that life does not happen spontaneously now, what do evolutionists assume?
3, 4. (a) What outline has been given of the steps leading to the origin of life? (b) In spite of the improbability of life originating by chance, what do evolutionists maintain?

38

beginning, Earth had an atmosphere composed of carbon dioxide, methane, ammonia and water. Through energy supplied by sunlight, and perhaps by lightning and exploding volcanoes, these simple compounds were broken apart and then they re-formed into amino acids. A variety of these gradu-ally accumulated in the sea and combined into pro-teinlike compounds. Ultimately, he says, the ocean became an "organic soup," but still lifeless.

[4] Then, according to Dawkins' description, "a par-ticularly remarkable molecule was formed by acci-dent"—a molecule that had the ability to reproduce itself. Though admitting that such an accident was exceedingly improbable, he maintains that it must nevertheless have happened. Similar molecules clustered together, and then, again by an exceed-ingly improbable accident, they wrapped a protec-tive barrier of other protein molecules around themselves as a membrane. Thus, it is claimed, the first living cell generated itself.[2]

[5] At this point a reader may begin to understand Dawkins' comment in the preface to his book: "This book should be read almost as though it were science fiction."[3] But readers on the subject will find that his approach is not unique. Most other books on evolution also skim over the staggering problem of explaining the emergence of life from nonliving matter. Thus Professor William Thorpe of the zoology department of Cambridge University told fellow scientists: "All the facile speculations and discussions published during the last ten to fifteen years explaining the mode of origin of life have been shown to be far too simple-minded and to bear very little weight. The problem in fact seems as far from solution as it ever was."[4]

[6] The recent explosive increase of knowledge has only served to magnify the gulf between nonliving

---

5. How is the origin of life usually dealt with in published mate-rial, yet what does a scientist say?
6. What does increasing knowledge show?

and living things. Even the oldest known single-celled organisms have been found to be incomprehensibly complex. "The problem for biology is to reach a simple beginning," say astronomers Fred Hoyle and Chandra Wickramasinghe. "Fossil residues of ancient life-forms discovered in the rocks do not reveal a simple beginning. . . . so the evolutionary theory lacks a proper foundation."[5] And as information increases, the harder it becomes to explain how microscopic forms of life that are so incredibly complex could have arisen by chance.

[7] The principal steps en route to the origin of life, as envisioned by evolutionary theory, are (1) the existence of the right primitive atmosphere and (2) a concentration in the oceans of an organic soup of "simple" molecules necessary for life. (3) From these come proteins and nucleotides (complex chemical compounds) that (4) combine and acquire a membrane, and thereafter (5) they develop a genetic code and start making copies of themselves. Are these steps in accord with the available facts?

The Primitive Atmosphere

[8] In 1953 Stanley Miller passed an electric spark through an "atmosphere" of hydrogen, methane, ammonia and water vapor. This produced some of the many amino acids that exist and that are the building blocks of proteins. However, he got just 4 of the 20 amino acids needed for life to exist. More than 30 years later, scientists were still unable experimentally to produce all the 20 necessary amino acids under conditions that could be considered plausible.

[9] Miller assumed that earth's primitive atmo-

No large building could stand without a foundation. "The evolutionary theory lacks a proper foundation," say two scientists

---

7. What are the claimed principal steps en route to the origin of life?
8. How did a famous experiment by Stanley Miller, and later ones, fall short?
9, 10. (a) What is believed regarding the possible composition of earth's primitive atmosphere? (b) What dilemma does evolution face, and what is known about earth's primitive atmosphere?

sphere was similar to the one in his experimental flask. Why? Because, as he and a co-worker later said: "The synthesis of compounds of biological interest takes place only under reducing [no free oxygen in the atmosphere] conditions."[6] Yet other evolutionists theorize that oxygen was present. The dilemma this creates for evolution is expressed by Hitching: "With oxygen in the air, the first amino acid would never have got started; without oxygen, it would have been wiped out by cosmic rays."[7]

[10] The fact is, any attempt to establish the nature of earth's primitive atmosphere can only be based on guesswork or assumption. No one knows for sure what it was like.

Would an "Organic Soup" Form?

[11] How likely is it that the amino acids thought to have formed in the atmosphere would drift down and form an "organic soup" in the oceans? Not likely at all. The same energy that would split the simple compounds in the atmosphere would even more quickly decompose any complex amino acids that formed. Interestingly, in his experiment of passing an electric spark through an "atmosphere," Miller saved the four amino acids he got only because he removed them from the area of the spark. Had he left them there, the spark would have decomposed them.

[12] However, if it is assumed that amino acids somehow reached the oceans and were protected from the destructive ultraviolet radiation in the atmosphere, what then? Hitching explained: "Beneath the surface of the water there would not be enough energy to activate further chemical reactions; water in any case inhibits the growth of more complex molecules."[8]

---

11. (a) Why is it unlikely that an "organic soup" would accumulate in the ocean? (b) How was Miller able to save the few amino acids he did get?
12. What would happen to amino acids even if some reached the oceans?

All red, all the right variety, each one in its preassigned place —by chance?

[13] So once amino acids are in the water, they must get out of it if they are to form larger molecules and evolve toward becoming proteins useful for the formation of life. But once they get out of the water, they are in the destructive ultraviolet light again! "In other words," Hitching says, "the theoretical chances of getting through even this first and relatively easy stage [getting amino acids] in the evolution of life are forbidding."[9]

[14] Although it commonly is asserted that life spontaneously arose in the oceans, bodies of water simply are not conducive to the necessary chemistry. Chemist Richard Dickerson explains: "It is therefore hard to see how polymerization [linking together smaller molecules to form bigger ones] could have proceeded in the aqueous environment of the primitive ocean, since the presence of water favors depolymerization [breaking up big molecules into simpler ones] rather than polymerization."[10] Biochemist George Wald agrees with this view, stating: "Spontaneous dissolution is much more probable, and hence proceeds much more rapidly, than spontaneous synthesis." This means there would be no accumulation of organic soup! Wald believes this to be "the most stubborn problem that confronts us [evolutionists]."[11]

13. What must amino acids in water do if they are to form proteins, but then what other danger do they face?
14. So, what is one of the most stubborn problems facing evolutionists?

42

[15] There is, however, another stubborn problem that confronts evolutionary theory. Remember, there are over 100 amino acids, but only 20 are needed for life's proteins. Moreover, they come in two shapes: Some of the molecules are "right-handed" and others are "left-handed." Should they be formed at random, as in a theoretical organic soup, it is most likely that half would be right-handed and half left-handed. And there is no known reason why either shape should be preferred in living things. Yet, of the 20 amino acids used in producing life's proteins, *all* are left-handed!

[16] How is it that, at random, only the specifically required kinds would be united in the soup? Physicist J. D. Bernal acknowledges: "It must be admitted that the explanation . . . still remains one of the most difficult parts of the structural aspects of life to explain." He concluded: "We may never be able to explain it."[12]

Life's use of only "left-handed" amino acids: "We may never be able to explain it"

Probability and Spontaneous Proteins

[17] What chance is there that the correct amino acids would come together to form a protein molecule? It could be likened to having a big, thoroughly mixed pile containing equal numbers of red beans and white beans. There are also over 100 different varieties of beans. Now, if you plunged a scoop into this pile, what do you think you would get? To get the beans that represent the basic components of a protein, you would have to scoop up only red ones—no white ones at all! Also, your scoop must contain only 20 varieties of the red beans, and each one must be in a specific, pre-assigned place in the scoop. In the world of protein, a single mistake in any one of these requirements would cause the protein that is produced to fail to function properly. Would any amount of stirring

---

15, 16. What major problem is there in getting life's proteins from the amino acids in a supposed organic soup?
17. What illustration shows the extent of the problem?

and scooping in our hypothetical bean pile have given the right combination? No. Then how would it have been possible in the hypothetical organic soup?

[18] The proteins needed for life have very complex molecules. What is the chance of even a simple protein molecule forming at random in an organic soup? Evolutionists acknowledge it to be only one in 10^{113} (1 followed by 113 zeros). But any event that has one chance in just 10^{50} is dismissed by mathematicians as never happening. An idea of the odds, or probability, involved is seen in the fact that the number 10^{113} is larger than the estimated total number of all the atoms in the universe!

"Proteins depend on DNA for their formation. But DNA cannot form without pre-existing protein"

[19] Some proteins serve as structural materials and others as enzymes. The latter speed up needed chemical reactions in the cell. Without such help, the cell would die. Not just a few, but 2,000 proteins serving as enzymes are needed for the cell's activity. What are the chances of obtaining all of these at random? One chance in $10^{40,000}$! "An outrageously small probability," Hoyle asserts, "that could not be faced even if the whole universe consisted of organic soup." He adds: "If one is not prejudiced either by social beliefs or by a scientific training into the conviction that life originated [spontaneously] on the Earth, this simple calculation wipes the idea entirely out of court."[13]

[20] However, the chances actually are far fewer than this "outrageously small" figure indicates. There must be a membrane enclosing the cell. But this membrane is extremely complex, made up of protein, sugar and fat molecules. As evolutionist Leslie Orgel writes: "Modern cell membranes include channels and pumps which specifically con-

---

18. How realistic are the odds of even a simple protein molecule forming by chance?
19. What chance is there of getting the needed enzymes for a living cell?
20. Why does the membrane needed by the cell add to the problem?

44

Which came first?

trol the influx and efflux of nutrients, waste products, metal ions and so on. These specialised channels involve highly specific proteins, molecules that could not have been present at the very beginning of the evolution of life."[14]

The Remarkable Genetic Code

[21] More difficult to obtain than these are nucleotides, the structural units of DNA, which bears the genetic code. Five histones are involved in DNA (histones are thought to be involved in governing the activity of genes). The chance of forming even the simplest of these histones is said to be one in 20^{100} —another huge number "larger than the total of all the atoms in all the stars and galaxies visible in the largest astronomical telescopes."[15]

[22] Yet greater difficulties for evolutionary theory involve the origin of the complete genetic code—a requirement for cell reproduction. The old puzzle of 'the chicken or the egg' rears its head relative to proteins and DNA. Hitching says: "Proteins depend on DNA for their formation. But DNA cannot form without pre-existing protein."[16] This leaves the paradox Dickerson raises: "Which came first," the protein or the DNA? He asserts: "The answer must be,

"The origin of the genetic code poses a massive chicken-and-egg problem that remains, at present, completely scrambled"

21. How difficult would it be to get the histones the DNA requires?
22. (a) How is the old puzzle of 'the chicken or the egg' related to proteins and DNA? (b) What solution is offered by one evolutionist, and is this reasonable?

45

'They developed in parallel.'"[17] In effect, he is saying that 'the chicken' and 'the egg' must have evolved simultaneously, neither one coming from the other. Does this strike you as reasonable? A science writer sums it up: "The origin of the genetic code poses a massive chicken-and-egg problem that remains, at present, completely scrambled."[18]

[23] Chemist Dickerson also made this interesting comment: "The evolution of the genetic machinery is the step for which there are no laboratory models; hence one can speculate endlessly, unfettered by inconvenient facts."[19] But is it good scientific procedure to brush aside the avalanches of "inconvenient facts" so easily? Leslie Orgel calls the existence of the genetic code "the most baffling aspect of the problem of the origins of life."[20] And Francis Crick concluded: "In spite of the genetic code being almost universal, the mechanism necessary to embody it is far too complex to have arisen in one blow."[21]

The genetic code: "the most baffling aspect of the problem of the origins of life"

[24] Evolutionary theory attempts to eliminate the need for the impossible to be accomplished "in one blow" by espousing a step-by-step process by which natural selection could do its work gradually. However, without the genetic code to begin reproduction, there can be no material for natural selection to select.

Amazing Photosynthesis

[25] An additional hurdle for evolutionary theory now arises. Somewhere along the line the primitive cell had to devise something that revolutionized life on earth—photosynthesis. This process, by which plants take in carbon dioxide and give off oxygen, is not yet completely understood by scientists. It is, as biologist F. W. Went states, "a process that no

---

23. What do other scientists say about the genetic machinery?
24. What can be said about natural selection and the first reproducing cell?
25. Evolution attributes to a simple cell the amazing ability to originate what process?

Humans and animals breathe in oxygen, give off carbon dioxide. Plants take in carbon dioxide, give off oxygen

Light

Oxygen   Water vapor   Carbon dioxide

one has yet been able to reproduce in a test tube."[22] Yet, by chance, a tiny simple cell is thought to have originated it.

[26] This process of photosynthesis turned an atmosphere that contained no free oxygen into one in which one molecule out of every five is oxygen. As a result, animals could breathe oxygen and live, and an ozone layer could form to protect all life from the damaging effects of ultraviolet radiation. Could this remarkable array of circumstances be accounted for simply by random chance?

Is Intelligence Involved?

[27] When confronted with the astronomical odds against a living cell forming by chance, some evolutionists feel forced to back away. For example, the authors of *Evolution From Space* (Hoyle and Wickramasinghe) give up, saying: "These issues are too complex to set numbers to." They add: "There is no way . . . in which we can simply get by with a bigger and better organic soup, as we ourselves hoped might be possible a year or two ago. The numbers we calculated above are essentially just as unfaceable for a universal soup as for a terrestrial one."[23]

In photosynthesis plants use sunlight, carbon dioxide, water and minerals to produce oxygen and food products. Could a simple cell have invented all of this?

---

26. What revolutionary change did this process cause?
27. Where has the evidence left some evolutionists?

The Incredible Cell

A living cell is enormously complex. Biologist Francis Crick endeavors to describe its workings simply, but he finally realizes that he can go only so far, "because it is so complicated the reader should not attempt to struggle with all the details."[a]

The instructions within the DNA of the cell, "if written out, would fill a thousand 600-page books," explains *National Geographic.* "Each cell is a world brimming with as many as two hundred trillion tiny groups of atoms called molecules. . . . Our 46 chromosome 'threads' linked together would measure more than six feet. Yet the nucleus that contains them is less than four ten-thousandths of an inch in diameter."[b]

Newsweek magazine uses an illustration to give an idea of the cell's activities: "Each of those 100 trillion cells functions like a walled city. Power plants generate the cell's energy. Factories produce proteins, vital units of chemical commerce. Complex transportation systems guide specific chemicals from point to point within the cell and beyond. Sentries at the barricades control the export and import markets, and monitor the outside world for signs of danger. Disciplined biological armies stand ready to grapple with invaders. A centralized genetic government maintains order."[c]

When the modern theory of evolution was first proposed, scientists had little inkling of the fantastic complexity of a living cell. On the facing page are a few of the parts of a typical cell—all packed into a container only 1/1000 inch across.

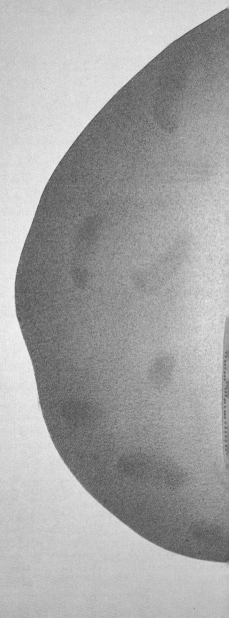

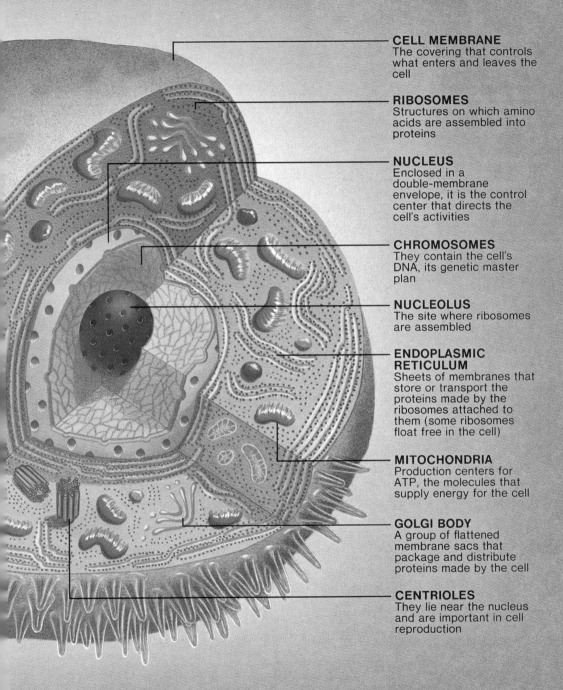

CELL MEMBRANE
The covering that controls what enters and leaves the cell

RIBOSOMES
Structures on which amino acids are assembled into proteins

NUCLEUS
Enclosed in a double-membrane envelope, it is the control center that directs the cell's activities

CHROMOSOMES
They contain the cell's DNA, its genetic master plan

NUCLEOLUS
The site where ribosomes are assembled

ENDOPLASMIC RETICULUM
Sheets of membranes that store or transport the proteins made by the ribosomes attached to them (some ribosomes float free in the cell)

MITOCHONDRIA
Production centers for ATP, the molecules that supply energy for the cell

GOLGI BODY
A group of flattened membrane sacs that package and distribute proteins made by the cell

CENTRIOLES
They lie near the nucleus and are important in cell reproduction

— Did Your 100,000,000,000,000 Cells Just Happen?

[28] Hence, after acknowledging that intelligence must somehow have been involved in bringing life into existence, the authors continue: "Indeed, such a theory is so obvious that one wonders why it is not widely accepted as being self-evident. The reasons are psychological rather than scientific."[24] Thus an observer might conclude that a "psychological" barrier is the only plausible explanation as to why most evolutionists cling to a chance origin for life and reject any "design or purpose or directedness,"[25] as Dawkins expressed it. Indeed, even Hoyle and Wickramasinghe, after acknowledging the need for intelligence, say that they do not believe a personal Creator is responsible for the origin of life.[26] In their thinking, intelligence is mandatory, but a Creator is unacceptable. Do you find that contradictory?

Some scientists say, in effect: 'Intelligence is mandatory, but a Creator is unacceptable'

Is It Scientific?

[29] If a spontaneous beginning for life is to be accepted as scientific fact, it should be established by the scientific method. This has been described as follows: Observe what happens; based on those observations, form a theory as to what may be true; test the theory by further observations and by experiments; and watch to see if the predictions based on the theory are fulfilled.

[30] In an attempt to apply the scientific method, it has not been possible to observe the spontaneous generation of life. There is no evidence that it is happening now, and of course no human observer was around when evolutionists say it was happening. No theory concerning it has been verified by observation. Laboratory experiments have failed to

---

28. (a) What probably lies behind the refusal to acknowledge the need for intelligence? (b) What do evolutionists who believe in the need for higher intelligence say is not the source of that intelligence?
29. What is the scientific method?
30. In what ways does spontaneous generation fall short in reference to applying the scientific method?

repeat it. Predictions based on the theory have not been fulfilled. With such an inability to apply the scientific method, is it honest science to elevate such a theory to the level of fact?

31 On the other hand, there is ample evidence to support the conclusion that the spontaneous generation of life from nonliving matter is not possible. "One has only to contemplate the magnitude of this task," Professor Wald of Harvard University acknowledges, "to concede that the spontaneous generation of a living organism is impossible." But what does this proponent of evolution actually believe? He answers: "Yet here we are—as a result, I believe, of spontaneous generation."[27] Does that sound like objective science?

32 British biologist Joseph Henry Woodger characterized such reasoning as "simple dogmatism—asserting that what you want to believe did in fact happen."[28] How have scientists come to accept in their own minds this apparent violation of the scientific method? The well-known evolutionist Loren Eiseley conceded: "After having chided the theologian for his reliance on myth and miracle, science found itself in the unenviable position of having to create a mythology of its own: namely, the assumption that what, after long effort, could not be proved to take place today had, in truth, taken place in the primeval past."[29]

33 Based on the evidence, the spontaneous generation of life theory appears better to fit the realm of science fiction than scientific fact. Many supporters apparently have forsaken the scientific method in such matters in order to believe what they want to believe. In spite of the overwhelming

---

31. What contradictory views about spontaneous generation does a scientist have?
32. How do even evolutionists admit that such reasoning is unscientific?
33. Based on all the preceding evidence, what conclusion must be reached concerning spontaneous generation and the application of the scientific method?

Evolutionists past and present comment on the origin of life

"The hypothesis that life has developed from inorganic matter is, at present, still an article of faith."—Mathematician J. W. N. Sullivan[d]

"The probability of life originating from accident is comparable to the probability of the unabridged dictionary resulting from an explosion in a printing shop."—Biologist Edwin Conklin[e]

"One has only to contemplate the magnitude of this task to concede that the spontaneous generation of a living organism is impossible."—Biochemist George Wald[f]

"An honest man, armed with all the knowledge available to us now, could only state that in some sense, the origin of life appears at the moment to be almost a miracle."—Biologist Francis Crick[g]

"If one is not prejudiced either by social beliefs or by a scientific training into the conviction that life originated [spontaneously] on the Earth, this simple calculation [the mathematical odds against it] wipes the idea entirely out of court."—Astronomers Fred Hoyle and N. C. Wickramasinghe[h]

odds against life originating by chance, unyielding dogmatism prevails rather than the caution normally signaled by the scientific method.

Not All Scientists Accept It

[34] Not all scientists, however, have closed the door on the alternative. For example, physicist H. S. Lipson, realizing the odds against a spontaneous origin for life, said: "The only acceptable explana-

---

34. (a) How does a physicist demonstrate scientific openness? (b) How does he describe evolution, and what commentary does he make about many scientists?

tion is *creation*. I know that this is anathema to physicists, as indeed it is to me, but we must not reject a theory that we do not like if the experimental evidence supports it." He further observed that after Darwin's book, *The Origin of Species,* "evolution became in a sense a scientific religion; almost all scientists have accepted it and many are prepared to 'bend' their observations to fit in with it."[30] A sad but true commentary.

[35] Chandra Wickramasinghe, professor at University College, Cardiff, said: "From my earliest training as a scientist I was very strongly brainwashed to believe that science cannot be consistent with any kind of deliberate creation. That notion has had to be very painfully shed. I am quite uncomfortable in the situation, the state of mind I now find myself in. But there is no logical way out of it. . . . For life to have been a chemical accident on earth is like looking for a particular grain of sand on all the beaches in all the planets in the universe—and finding it." In other words, it is just not possible that life could have originated from a chemical accident. So Wickramasinghe concludes: "There is no other way in which we can understand the precise ordering of the chemicals of life except to invoke the creations on a cosmic scale."[31]

> A scientist admitted: "The only acceptable explanation is *creation*"

[36] As astronomer Robert Jastrow said: "Scientists have no proof that life was not the result of an act of creation."[32]

[37] Yet, even assuming that a first living cell did somehow spontaneously arise, is there evidence that it evolved into all the creatures that have ever lived on the earth? Fossils supply the answer, and the next chapter considers what the fossil record really says.

> Jastrow: "Scientists have no proof that life was not the result of an act of creation"

---

35. (a) What notion has a university professor found it painful to shed? (b) How does he illustrate the possibility of life evolving by chance?
36. What comment does Robert Jastrow make?
37. What question is raised concerning evolution, and where can the answer be found?

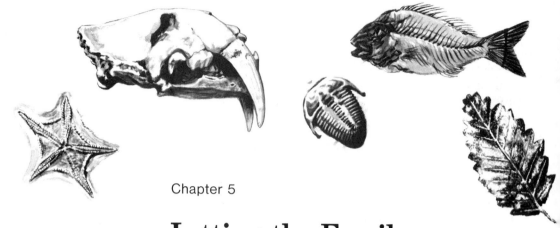

Chapter 5

Letting the Fossil Record Speak

FOSSILS are the remains of ancient forms of life preserved in the earth's crust. These may be skeletons or parts of them such as bones, teeth or shells. A fossil also may be some trace of the activity of what was once alive, such as an imprint or trail. Many fossils no longer contain their original material but are made up of mineral deposits that have infiltrated them and have taken on their shape.

[2] Why are fossils important to evolution? Geneticist G. L. Stebbins noted a major reason: "No biologist has actually seen the origin by evolution of a major group of organisms."[1] So, living things on earth today are not seen to be evolving into something else. Instead, they are all complete in form and distinct from other types. As geneticist Theodosius Dobzhansky observed: "The living world is not a single array . . . connected by unbroken series of intergrades."[2] And Charles Darwin conceded that "the distinctness of specific [living] forms and their not being blended together by innumerable transitional links, is a very obvious difficulty."[3]

"No biologist has actually seen the origin by evolution of a major group of organisms"

[3] Thus, the distinct varieties of things now alive offer no support to the theory of evolution. That is why the fossil record became so important. It was

1. What are fossils?
2, 3. Why are fossils important to evolution?

Orthodox evolutionary theory anticipated a fossil record that contains:	The creation pattern anticipated a fossil record that contains:
1. Very simple life forms gradually appearing	1. Complex life forms suddenly appearing
2. Simple forms gradually changing into complex ones	2. Complex life forms multiplying 'after their kinds' (biological families), though allowing for variety
3. Many transitional "links" between different kinds	3. No transitional "links" between different biological families
4. Beginnings of new body features, such as limbs, bones, organs	4. No partial body features; all parts complete

felt that at least fossils would provide the confirmation that the theory of evolution needed.

What to Look For

[4] If evolution were a fact, the fossil evidence would surely reveal a gradual changing from one kind of life into another. And that would have to be the case regardless of which variation of evolutionary theory is accepted. Even scientists who believe in the more rapid changes associated with the "punctuated equilibrium" theory acknowledge that there would still have been many thousands of years during which these changes supposedly took place. So it is not reasonable to believe that there would be no need at all for linking fossils.

[5] Also, if evolution were founded in fact, the fossil record would be expected to reveal beginnings of new structures in living things. There should be at least some fossils with developing arms, legs,

---

4-6. If evolution were factual, what would the fossil evidence show?

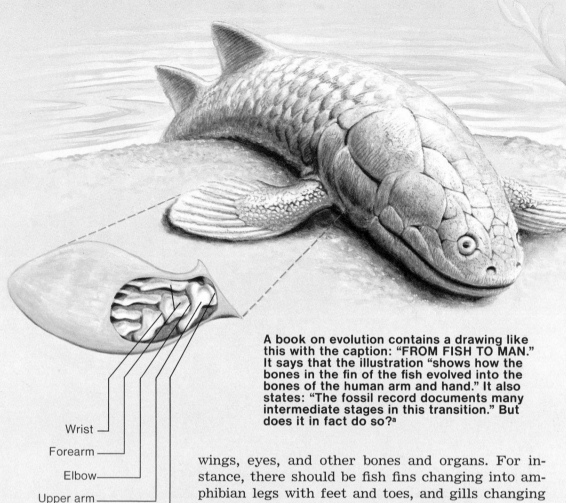

Wrist
Forearm
Elbow
Upper arm
Shoulder

A book on evolution contains a drawing like this with the caption: "FROM FISH TO MAN." It says that the illustration "shows how the bones in the fin of the fish evolved into the bones of the human arm and hand." It also states: "The fossil record documents many intermediate stages in this transition." But does it in fact do so?[a]

wings, eyes, and other bones and organs. For instance, there should be fish fins changing into amphibian legs with feet and toes, and gills changing into lungs. There should be reptiles with front limbs changing into bird wings, back limbs changing into legs with claws, scales changing into feathers, and mouths changing into horny beaks.

[6] In this regard the British journal *New Scientist* says of the theory: "It predicts that a complete fossil record would consist of lineages of organisms showing gradual change continuously over long periods of time."[4] As Darwin himself asserted: "The number of intermediate varieties, which have formerly existed, [must] be truly enormous."[5]

[7] On the other hand, if the Genesis creation account is factual, then the fossil record would *not*

---

7. What should the fossil record show if the Genesis creation account is factual?

56

show one type of life turning into another. It would reflect the Genesis statement that each different type of living thing would reproduce only "according to its kind." (Genesis 1:11, 12, 21, 24, 25) Also, if living things came into being by an act of creation, there would be no partial, unfinished bones or organs in the fossil record. All fossils would be complete and highly complex, as living things are today.

[8] In addition, if living things were created, they would be expected to appear suddenly in the fossil record, unconnected to anything before them. And if this was found to be true, what then? Darwin frankly admitted: "If numerous species . . . have really started into life at once, the fact would be fatal to the theory of evolution."[6]

How Complete Is the Record?

[9] However, is the fossil record complete enough for a fair test of whether it is creation or evolution that finds support? Over a century ago, Darwin did not think so. What was "wrong" with the fossil record in his time? It did not contain the transitional links required to support his theory. This situation caused him to say: "Why then is not every geological formation and every stratum full of such intermediate links? Geology assuredly does not reveal any such finely-graduated organic chain; and this, perhaps, is the most obvious and serious objection which can be urged against the theory."[7]

[10] The fossil record in Darwin's day proved disappointing to him in another way. He explained: "The abrupt manner in which whole groups of species suddenly appear in certain formations has been urged by several paleontologists . . . as a fatal objection to the belief in the transmutation of spe-

Darwin: "If numerous species . . . have really started into life at once, the fact would be fatal to the theory of evolution"

---

8. If living things were created, what else should the fossil record show?
9. What did Darwin say about the evidence in his day?
10. What other disappointment did Darwin mention?

57

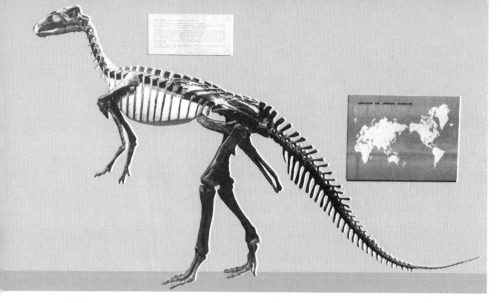

Millions of fossils have been found and are in museums and laboratories around the world

cies." He added: "There is another and allied difficulty, which is much more serious. I allude to the manner in which species belonging to several of the main divisions of the animal kingdom suddenly appear in the lowest known fossiliferous rocks. . . . The case at present must remain inexplicable; and may be truly urged as a valid argument against the [evolutionary] views here entertained."[8]

[11] Darwin attempted to explain these huge problems by attacking the fossil record. He said: "I look at the geological record as a history of the world imperfectly kept, . . . imperfect to an extreme degree."[9] It was assumed by him and others that as time passed the missing fossil links surely would be found.

[12] Now, after well over a century of extensive digging, vast numbers of fossils have been unearthed. Is the record still so "imperfect"? The book *Processes of Organic Evolution* comments: "The record of past forms of life is now extensive and is constantly increasing in richness as paleontologists find, describe, and compare new fossils."[10] And Smithsonian Institution scientist Porter Kier adds: "There are a hundred million fossils, all catalogued and identified, in museums around the

11. How did Darwin attempt to explain the difficulties?
12. How extensive is the fossil record now?

58

world."[11] Hence, *A Guide to Earth History* declares: "By the aid of fossils palaeontologists can now give us an excellent picture of the life of past ages."[12]

[13] After all this time, and the assembling of millions of fossils, what does the record now say? Evolutionist Steven Stanley states that these fossils "reveal new and surprising things about our biological origins."[13] The book *A View of Life,* written by three evolutionists, adds: "The fossil record is full of trends that paleontologists have been unable to explain."[14] What is it that these evolutionary scientists have found to be so "surprising" and are "unable to explain"?

[14] What has confounded such scientists is the fact that the massive fossil evidence now available reveals the very same thing that it did in Darwin's day: Basic kinds of living things appeared suddenly and did not change appreciably for long periods of time. No transitional links between one major kind of living thing and another have ever been found. So what the fossil record says is just the opposite of what was expected.

The fossil record says the opposite of what evolutionary theory had predicted

[15] Swedish botanist Heribert Nilsson described the situation this way, after 40 years of his own research: "It is not even possible to make a caricature of an evolution out of palaeobiological facts. The fossil material is now so complete that . . . the lack of transitional series cannot be explained as due to the scarcity of material. The deficiencies are real, they will never be filled."[15]

Life Appears Suddenly

[16] Let us take a closer look at the evidence. In his book *Red Giants and White Dwarfs* Robert Jastrow states: "Sometime in the first billion years, life

---

13, 14. Why have evolutionists been disappointed by the enlarged fossil evidence?
15. What conclusion did a botanist draw from his study of the fossil record?
16. (a) What does a scientist lead one to expect about the early fossil record? (b) Does the fossil record fulfill that expectation?

appeared on the earth's surface. Slowly, the fossil record indicates, living organisms climbed the ladder from simple to more advanced forms." From this description, one would expect that the fossil record has verified a slow evolution from the first "simple" life forms to complex ones. Yet, the same book says: "The critical first billion years, during which life began, are blank pages in the earth's history."[16]

[17] Also, can those first types of life truly be described as "simple"? "Going back in time to the age of the oldest rocks," says *Evolution From Space,* "fossil residues of ancient life-forms discovered in the rocks do not reveal a simple beginning. Although we may care to think of fossil bacteria and fossil algae and microfungi as being simple compared to a dog or horse, the information standard remains enormously high. Most of the biochemical complexity of life was present already at the time the oldest surface rocks of the Earth were formed."[17]

"Fossil residues of ancient life-forms discovered in the rocks do not reveal a simple beginning"

[18] From this beginning, can any evidence at all be found to verify that one-celled organisms evolved into many-celled ones? "The fossil record contains no trace of these preliminary stages in the development of many-celled organisms," says Jastrow.[18] Instead, he states: "The record of the rocks contains very little, other than bacteria and one-celled plants until, about a billion years ago, after some three billion years of invisible progress, a major breakthrough occurred. The first many-celled creatures appeared on earth."[19]

[19] Thus, at the start of what is called the Cambrian period, the fossil record takes an unexplained dramatic turn. A great variety of fully developed,

17. Could the first forms of life be called "simple"?
18. Is there any fossil evidence that one-celled creatures evolved into many-celled ones?
19. What happened at the start of what is called the Cambrian period?

Sponge

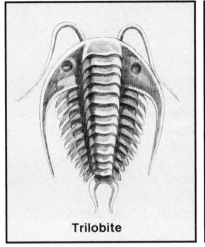

Trilobite

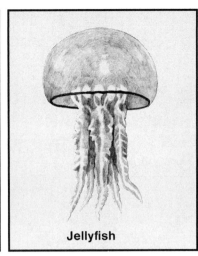

Jellyfish

Early in what is called the Cambrian period, fossils of the major groups of invertebrates appear in a spectacular "explosion" of living things, unconnected to any evolutionary ancestors

complex sea creatures, many with hard outer shells, appear so suddenly that this time is often called an "explosion" of living things. *A View of Life* describes it: "Beginning at the base of the Cambrian period and extending for about 10 million years, all the major groups of skeletonized invertebrates made their first appearance in the most spectacular rise in diversity ever recorded on our planet." Snails, sponges, starfish, lobsterlike animals called trilobites, and many other complex sea creatures appeared. Interestingly, the same book observes: "Some extinct trilobites, in fact, developed more complex and efficient eyes than any living arthropod possesses."[20]

[20] Are there fossil links between this outburst of life and what went before it? In Darwin's time such links did not exist. He admitted: "To the question why we do not find rich fossiliferous deposits belonging to these assumed earliest periods prior to the Cambrian system, I can give no satisfactory answer."[21] Today, has the situation changed? Paleontologist Alfred S. Romer noted Darwin's statement about "the abrupt manner in which whole groups of species suddenly appear" and wrote: "Be-

Darwin: "Whole groups of species suddenly appear"

20. Are there any fossil links between the Cambrian outburst of life and what went before it?

low this [Cambrian period], there are vast thicknesses of sediments in which the progenitors of the Cambrian forms would be expected. But we do not find them; these older beds are almost barren of evidence of life, and the general picture could reasonably be said to be consistent with the idea of a special creation at the beginning of Cambrian times. 'To the question why we do not find rich fossiliferous deposits belonging to these assumed earliest periods prior to the Cambrian system,' said Darwin, 'I can give no satisfactory answer.' Nor can we today," said Romer.[22]

[21] Some argue that Precambrian rocks were too altered by heat and pressure to retain fossil links, or that no rocks were deposited in shallow seas for fossils to be retained. "Neither of these arguments has held up," say evolutionists Salvador E. Luria, Stephen Jay Gould and Sam Singer. They add: "Geologists have discovered many unaltered Precambrian sediments, and they contain no fossils of complex organisms."[23]

[22] These facts prompted biochemist D. B. Gower to comment, as related in England's Kentish *Times:* "The creation account in Genesis and the theory of evolution could not be reconciled. One must be right and the other wrong. The story of the fossils agreed with the account of Genesis. In the oldest rocks we did not find a series of fossils covering the gradual changes from the most primitive creatures to developed forms, but rather in the oldest rocks, developed species suddenly appeared. Between every species there was a complete absence of intermediate fossils."[24]

[23] Zoologist Harold Coffin concluded: "If progressive evolution from simple to complex is correct, the ancestors of these full-blown living creatures in the Cambrian should be found; but they have not

"The general picture could reasonably be said to be consistent with the idea of a special creation"

"There was a complete absence of intermediate fossils"

---

21. What arguments have not held up, and why not?
22. In view of these facts, what comments did a biochemist make?
23. What did a zoologist conclude?

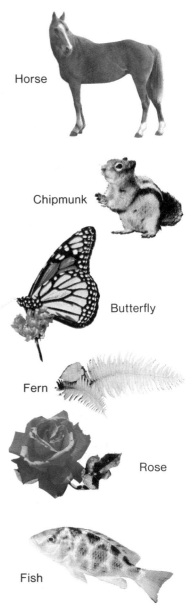

Horse

Chipmunk

Butterfly

Fern

Rose

Fish

been found and scientists admit there is little prospect of their ever being found. On the basis of the facts alone, on the basis of what is actually found in the earth, the theory of a sudden creative act in which the major forms of life were established fits best."[25]

Continued Sudden Appearances, Little Change

[24] In the layers above that Cambrian outburst of life, the testimony of the fossil record is repeatedly the same: New kinds of animals and new kinds of plants appear suddenly, with no connection to anything that went before them. And once on the scene, they continue with little change. *The New Evolutionary Timetable* states: "The record now reveals that species typically survive for a hundred thousand generations, or even a million or more, without evolving very much. . . . After their origins, most species undergo little evolution before becoming extinct."[26]

[25] For example, insects appeared in the fossil record suddenly and plentifully, without any evolutionary ancestors. Nor have they changed much even down to this day. Regarding the finding of a fossil fly that was labeled "40 million years old," Dr. George Poinar, Jr., said: "The internal anatomy of these creatures is remarkably similar to what you find in flies today. The wings and legs and head, and even the cells inside, are very modern-looking."[27] And a report in *The Globe and Mail* of Toronto commented: "In 40 million years of struggling up the evolutionary ladder, they have made almost no discernible progress."[28]

[26] A similar picture exists for plants. Found in the rocks are fossil leaves of many trees and shrubs

Different and very complex life forms appear suddenly and fully developed

---

24. Is the testimony of the fossil record the same in layers above the Cambrian period?
25. Insects have shown what remarkable stability?
26. How do plants and animals show the same stability?

Tern

Hummingbird

Eagle

Evolutionary theory maintains that flying creatures evolved from transitional ancestors; but none have been found

that show very little difference from the leaves of such plants today: oak, walnut, hickory, grape, magnolia, palm and many others. Animal kinds follow the same pattern. The ancestors of those alive today appear in the fossil record suddenly and were much like their living counterparts. There are many variations, but all are easily identified as the same "kind." *Discover* magazine notes one such example: "The horseshoe crab . . . has existed on earth virtually unchanged for 200 million years."[29] Those that became extinct also followed the same pattern. Dinosaurs, for example, appear suddenly in the fossil record, with no links to any ancestors before them. They multiplied greatly, then became extinct.

[27] On this point the *Bulletin* of Chicago's Field Museum of Natural History states: "Species appear in the sequence very suddenly, show little or no change during their existence in the record, then abruptly go out of the record. And it is not always clear, in fact it's rarely clear, that the descendants were actually better adapted than their predecessors. In other words, biological improvement is hard to find."[30]

No Transitional Features

[28] Another difficulty for evolution is the fact that nowhere in the fossil record are found partially formed bones or organs that could be taken for the beginning of a new feature. For instance, there are fossils of various types of flying creatures—birds, bats, extinct pterodactyls. According to evolutionary theory, they must have evolved from transitional ancestors. But none of those transitional forms have been found. There is not a hint of them. Are there any fossils of giraffes with necks two thirds or three quarters as long as at present? Are there

27. What does one scientific publication say about evolutionary "improvement"?
28. Have transitional forms of bones and organs ever been found?

64

any fossils of birds evolving a beak from a reptile jaw? Is there any fossil evidence of fish developing an amphibian pelvis, or of fish fins turning into amphibian legs, feet and toes? The fact is, looking for such developing features in the fossil record has proved to be a fruitless quest.

[29] *New Scientist* noted that evolution "predicts that a complete fossil record would consist of lineages of organisms showing gradual change continuously over long periods of time." But it admitted: "Unfortunately, the fossil record does not meet this expectation, for individual species of fossils are rarely connected to one another by known intermediate forms. . . . known fossil species do indeed appear *not* to evolve even over millions of years."[31] And geneticist Stebbins writes: "No transitional forms are known between any of the major phyla of animals or plants." He speaks of "the large gaps which exist between many major categories of organisms."[32] "In fact," *The New Evolutionary Timetable* acknowledges, "the fossil record *does not convincingly document a single transition* from one species to another. Furthermore, species lasted for astoundingly long periods of time."[33]—Italics added.

No fossils of giraffes have been found with necks two thirds or three quarters as long as at present

[30] This agrees with the extensive study made by the Geological Society of London and the Palaeontological Association of England. Professor of natural science John N. Moore reported on the results: "Some 120 scientists, all specialists, prepared 30 chapters in a monumental work of over 800 pages to present the fossil record for plants and animals divided into about 2,500 groups. . . . Each major form or kind of plant and animal is shown to have a separate and distinct history from all the other forms or kinds! Groups of both plants and animals *appear suddenly* in the fossil record. . . . Whales, bats, horses, primates, elephants, hares, squirrels,

29. What do evolutionists now acknowledge about supposed transitional forms?
30. What does an extensive study confirm?

65

etc., all are as distinct at their first appearance as they are now. There is not a trace of a common ancestor, much less a link with any reptile, the supposed progenitor." Moore added: "No transitional forms have been found in the fossil record very probably because no transitional forms exist in fossil stage at all. Very likely, transitions between animal kinds and/or transitions between plant kinds have never occurred."[34]

[31] Thus, what was true in Darwin's day is just as true today. The evidence of the fossil record is still as zoologist D'Arcy Thompson said some years ago in his book *On Growth and Form:* "Darwinian evolution has not taught us how birds descend from reptiles, mammals from earlier quadrupeds, quadrupeds from fishes, nor vertebrates from the invertebrate stock. . . . to seek for stepping-stones across the gaps between is to seek in vain, for ever."[35]

What About the Horse?

[32] However, it has often been said that at least the horse is a classic example of evolution found in the fossil record. As *The World Book Encyclopedia* states: "Horses are among the best-documented examples of evolutionary development."[36] Illustrations of this begin with a very small animal and end with the large horse of today. But does the fossil evidence really support this?

[33] The *Encyclopædia Britannica* comments: "The evolution of the horse was never in a straight line."[37] In other words, nowhere does the fossil evidence show a gradual development from the small animal to the large horse. Evolutionist Hitching says of this foremost evolutionary model: "Once portrayed as simple and direct, it is now so complicated that accepting one version rather than anoth-

"The evolution of the horse was never in a straight line"

31. Does the fossil record say something different now from what it said in Darwin's day?
32. What is often presented as a classic example of evolution?
33. Does the fossil evidence really support evolution of the horse?

This rodentlike animal is said to be similar to *Eohippus,* the presumed ancestor of the horse. But there is no evidence that *Eohippus* evolved into something more horselike

er is more a matter of faith than rational choice. *Eohippus,* supposedly the earliest horse, and said by experts to be long extinct and known to us only through fossils, may in fact be alive and well and not a horse at all—a shy, fox-sized animal called a daman that darts about in the African bush."[38]

[34] Placing little *Eohippus* as the ancestor of the horse strains the imagination, especially in view of what *The New Evolutionary Timetable* says: "It was widely assumed that [*Eohippus*] had slowly but persistently turned into a more fully equine animal." But do the facts support this assumption? "The fossil species of [*Eohippus*] show little evidence of evolutionary modification," answers the book. It thus concedes, regarding the fossil record: "It fails to document the full history of the horse family."[39]

[35] So, some scientists now say that little *Eohippus* never was a type of horse or an ancestor of one. And each type of fossil put into the horse line showed remarkable stability, with no transitional forms between it and others that were thought to be evolutionary ancestors. Nor should it be surprising that there are fossils of horses of different sizes and shapes. Even today, horses vary from very small ponies to large plow horses. All are varieties within the horse family.

"The *Equus* group, which includes all living horses ... appears suddenly in the fossil record ... their origin is not documented by known fossil evidence"[b]

34, 35. (a) Why do some now question the place of *Eohippus?* (b) Have any evolutionary ancestors been found for the varieties of fossil horses?

What the Fossil Evidence Says . . .

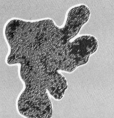

On the Origin of Life:

"For at least three-quarters of the book of ages engraved in the earth's crust the pages are blank."—*The World We Live In* [c]

"The initial steps . . . are not known; . . . no trace of them remains."—*Red Giants and White Dwarfs* [d]

On Many-Celled Life:

"How many-celled animals originated and whether this step occurred one or more times and in one or more ways remain difficult and ever-debated questions that are . . . 'in the last analysis, quite unanswerable.'"—*Science* [e]

"The fossil record contains no trace of these preliminary stages in the development of many-celled organisms."—*Red Giants and White Dwarfs* [f]

On Plant Life:

"Most botanists look to the fossil record as the source of enlightenment. But . . . no such help has been discovered. . . . There is no evidence of the ancestry."—*The Natural History of Palms* [g]

On Insects:

"The fossil record does not give any information on the origin of insects."—*Encyclopædia Britannica* [h]

"There are no fossils known that show what the primitive ancestral insects looked like."—*The Insects* [i]

On Animals With Backbones:

"Fossil remains, however, give no information on the origin of the vertebrates."—*Encyclopædia Britannica* [j]

On Fish:

"To our knowledge, no 'link' connected this new beast to any previous form of life. The fish just appeared."—*Marvels & Mysteries of Our Animal World* [k]

about the Origin of Living Things

On Fish Becoming Amphibians:

"Just how or why they did this we will probably never know."
— *The Fishes* [l]

On Amphibians Becoming Reptiles:

"One of the frustrating features of the fossil record of vertebrate history is that it shows so little about the evolution of reptiles during their earliest days, when the shelled egg was developing."— *The Reptiles* [m]

On Reptiles Becoming Mammals:

"There is no missing link [that connects] mammals and reptiles."— *The Reptiles* [n]

"Fossils, unfortunately, reveal very little about the creatures which we consider the first true mammals."— *The Mammals* [o]

On Reptiles Becoming Birds:

"The transition from reptiles to birds is more poorly documented."— *Processes of Organic Evolution* [p]

"No fossil of any such birdlike reptile has yet been found."
— *The World Book Encyclopedia* [q]

On Apes:

"Unfortunately, the fossil record which would enable us to trace the emergence of the apes is still hopelessly incomplete."— *The Primates* [r]

"Modern apes, for instance, seem to have sprung out of nowhere. They have no yesterday, no fossil record."— *Science Digest* [s]

From Ape to Man:

"No fossil or other physical evidence directly connects man to ape."— *Science Digest* [t]

"The human family does not consist of a solitary line of descent leading from an apelike form to our species."— *The New Evolutionary Timetable* [u]

69

What the Fossil Record Really Says

[36] When we let the fossil record speak, its testimony is not evolution-oriented. Instead, the testimony of the fossil record is creation-oriented. It shows that many different kinds of living things suddenly appeared. While there was great variety within each kind, these had no links to evolutionary ancestors before them. Nor did they have any evolutionary links to different kinds of living things that came after them. Various kinds of living things persisted with little change for long periods of time before some of them became extinct, while others survive down to this day.

"The concept of evolution cannot be considered a strong scientific explanation for the presence of the diverse forms of life"

[37] "The concept of evolution cannot be considered a strong scientific explanation for the presence of the diverse forms of life," concludes evolutionist Edmund Samuel in his book *Order: In Life*. Why not? He adds: "No fine analysis of biogeographic distribution or of the fossil record can directly support evolution."[40]

[38] Clearly, the impartial inquirer would be led to conclude that fossils do not support the theory of evolution. On the other hand, fossil evidence does lend strong weight to the arguments for creation. As zoologist Coffin stated: "To secular scientists, the fossils, evidences of the life of the past, constitute the ultimate and final court of appeal, because the fossil record is the only authentic history of life available to science. If this fossil history does not agree with evolutionary theory—and we have seen that it does not—what does it teach? It tells us that plants and animals were created in their basic forms. The basic facts of the fossil record support creation, not evolution."[41] Astronomer Carl Sagan candidly acknowledged in his book *Cosmos:* "The fossil evidence could be consistent with the idea of a Great Designer."[42]

---

36. What does the fossil record really show?
37. How does an evolutionist acknowledge this?
38. What would the impartial inquirer conclude?

Chapter 6

Huge Gulfs—
Can Evolution Bridge Them?

FOSSILS give tangible evidence of the varieties of life that existed long before man's arrival. But they have not produced the expected backing for the evolutionary view of how life began or how new kinds got started thereafter. Commenting on the lack of transitional fossils to bridge the biological gaps, Francis Hitching observes: "The curious thing is that there is a consistency about the fossil gaps: *the fossils go missing in all the important places.*"[1]

[2] The important places he refers to are the gaps between the major divisions of animal life. An example of this is that fish are thought to have evolved from the invertebrates, creatures without a backbone. "Fish jump into the fossil record," Hitching says, "seemingly from nowhere: mysteriously, suddenly, full formed."[2] Zoologist N. J. Berrill comments on his own evolutionary explanation of how the fish arrived, by saying: "In a sense this account is science fiction."[3]

[3] Evolutionary theory presumes that fish became amphibians, some amphibians became reptiles, from the reptiles came both mammals and birds, and eventually some mammals became men. The previous chapter has shown that the fossil record does not support these claims. This chapter will concen-

"Fish jump into the fossil record, seemingly from nowhere"

---

1. What is noted concerning gaps in the fossil record?
2. How do fossils of fish illustrate these gaps?
3. How does evolutionary theory chronicle the big divisions of animal life?

71

Backbones of fish and of frog are very different

No fossil fish show how the pelvis of amphibians developed

trate on the magnitude of the assumed transitional steps. As you read on, consider the likelihood of such changes happening spontaneously by undirected chance.

The Gulf Between Fish and Amphibian

[4] It was the backbone that distinguished the fish from the invertebrates. This backbone would have had to undergo major modifications for the fish to become amphibian, that is, a creature that could live both in the water and on land. A pelvis had to be added, but no fossil fish are known that show how the pelvis of amphibians developed. In some amphibians, such as frogs and toads, the entire backbone would have had to change beyond recognition. Also, skull bones are different. In addition, in the forming of amphibians, evolution requires fish fins to become jointed limbs with wrists and toes, accompanied by major alterations in muscles and nerves. Gills must change to lungs. In fish, blood is pumped by a two-chambered heart, but in amphibians by a three-chambered heart.

[5] To bridge the gap between fish and amphibian, the sense of hearing would have had to undergo a radical change. In general, fish receive sound through their bodies, but most toads and frogs have eardrums. Tongues would also have to change. No fish has an extendable tongue, but amphibians such as toads do. Amphibian eyes have the added ability to blink, since they have a membrane they pass over their eyeballs, keeping them clean.

[6] Strenuous efforts have been made to link the amphibians to some fish ancestor, but without success. The lungfish had been a favorite candidate, since, in addition to gills, it has a swim bladder, which can be used for breathing when it is tempo-

4, 5. What are some of the big differences between fish and amphibians?
6. What creatures had been considered links between fish and amphibians, and why are they not?

72

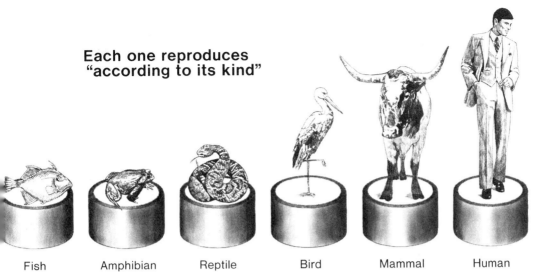

Each one reproduces "according to its kind"

Fish   Amphibian   Reptile   Bird   Mammal   Human

rarily out of the water. Says the book *The Fishes:* "It is tempting to think they might have some direct connection with the amphibians which led to the land-living vertebrates. But they do not; they are a separate group entirely."[4] David Attenborough disqualifies both the lungfish and the coelacanth "because the bones of their skulls are so different from those of the first fossil amphibians that the one cannot be derived from the other."[5]

There are no links between the major divisions of life. One scientist said: "The fossils go missing in all the important places"

The Gulf Between Amphibian and Reptile

[7] Trying to bridge the gap between amphibian and reptile poses other serious problems. A most difficult one is the origin of the shelled egg. Creatures prior to reptiles laid their soft, jellylike eggs in water, where the eggs were fertilized *externally*. Reptiles are land based and lay their eggs on land, but the developing embryos inside them must still be in a watery environment. The shelled egg was the answer. But it also required a major change in the process of fertilization: It called for *internal* fertilization, *before* the egg is surrounded by a shell. To accomplish this involved new sexual or-

---

7. From amphibian to reptile, what is one of the most difficult problems to explain?

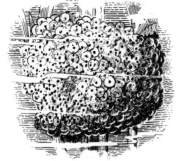

Jellylike eggs of amphibians have no shells

Eggs of reptiles have protective shells

Cross section of shelled egg

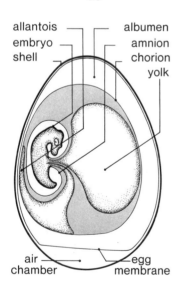

allantois — albumen
embryo — amnion
shell — chorion — yolk

air chamber — egg membrane

gans, new mating procedures and new instincts —all of which constitute a vast gulf between amphibian and reptile.

[8] Enclosing the egg in a shell made necessary further remarkable changes in order to make possible the development of a reptile and, finally, its release from the shell. For example, within the shell there is the need for various membranes and sacs, such as the amnion. This holds in the fluid in which the embryo grows. *The Reptiles* describes another membrane called the allantois: "The allantois receives and stores embryonic waste, serving as a sort of bladder. It also has blood vessels that pick up oxygen that passes through the shell and conduct it to the embryo."[6]

[9] Evolution has not accounted for other complex differences involved. Embryos in fish and amphibian eggs release their wastes in the surrounding water as soluble urea. But urea within the shelled eggs of reptiles would kill the embryos. So, in the shelled egg a major chemical change is made: The wastes, *insoluble* uric acid, are stored within the allantois membrane. Consider this also: The egg yolk is food for the growing reptile embryo, enabling it to develop fully before emerging from the shell—unlike amphibians, which do not hatch in the adult form. And to get out of the shell, the embryo is distinctive in having an egg tooth, to help it break out of its prison.

[10] Much more is needed to bridge the gap between amphibian and reptile, but these examples show that undirected chance just cannot account for all the many complex changes required to bridge that wide gulf. No wonder evolutionist Archie Carr lamented: "One of the frustrating features of the fossil record of vertebrate history is that it shows so little about the evolution of reptiles during

---

8, 9. What other features are necessary with the shelled egg?
10. What lament was raised by one evolutionist?

their earliest days, when the shelled egg was developing."[7]

The Gulf Between Reptile and Bird

[11] Reptiles are cold-blooded animals, meaning that their internal temperature will either increase or decrease depending upon the outside temperature. Birds, on the other hand, are warm-blooded; their bodies maintain a relatively constant internal temperature regardless of the temperature outside. To solve the puzzle of how warm-blooded birds came from cold-blooded reptiles, some evolutionists now say that some of the dinosaurs (which were reptiles) were warm-blooded. But the general view is still as Robert Jastrow observes: "Dinosaurs, like all reptiles, were cold-blooded animals."[8]

[12] Lecomte du Noüy, the French evolutionist, said concerning the belief that warm-blooded birds came from cold-blooded reptiles: "This stands out today as one of the greatest puzzles of evolution." He also made the admission that birds have "all the unsatisfactory characteristics of absolute creation"[9] —unsatisfactory, that is, to the theory of evolution.

Birds have "all the unsatisfactory characteristics of absolute creation"

[13] While it is true that both reptiles and birds lay eggs, only birds must incubate theirs. They are designed for it. Many birds have a brood spot on their breast, an area that does not have any feathers and that contains a network of blood vessels, to give warmth for the eggs. Some birds have no brood patch but they pull out the feathers from their breast. Also, for birds to incubate the eggs would require evolution to provide them with new instincts—for building the nest, for hatching the eggs and for feeding the young—very selfless, altruistic, considerate behaviors involving skill, hard work and deliberate exposure to danger. All of this

---

11, 12. What is a major difference between reptiles and birds, and how do some try to solve this puzzle?
13. What do birds do to incubate their eggs?

Parrot

Bird of paradise

Shaft

Barbs

Barbicels

Barbules

Peacock

Evolutionists state: "It takes no great stretch of imagination to envisage a feather as a modified [reptilian] scale." The facts show otherwise

represents a wide gap between reptiles and birds. But there is much more.

[14] Feathers are unique to birds. Supposedly, reptilian scales just happened to become these amazing structures. Out from the shaft of a feather are rows of barbs. Each barb has many barbules, and each barbule has hundreds of barbicels and hooklets. After a microscopic examination of one pigeon feather, it was revealed that it had "several hundred thousand barbules and millions of barbicels and hooklets."[10] These hooks hold all the parts of a feather together to make flat surfaces or vanes. Nothing excels the feather as an airfoil, and

14. What intricacies of feathers make it incredible that they could have come from reptilian scales?

76

few substances equal it as an insulator. A bird the size of a swan has some 25,000 feathers.

[15] If the barbs of these feathers become separated, they are combed with the beak. The beak applies pressure as the barbs pass through it, and the hooks on the barbules link together like the teeth of a zipper. Most birds have an oil gland at the base of the tail from which they take oil to condition each feather. Some birds have no oil gland but instead have special feathers that fray at their tips to produce a fine talclike dust for conditioning their feathers. And feathers usually are renewed by molting once a year.

[16] Knowing all of this about the feather, consider this rather astonishing effort to explain its development: "How did this structural marvel evolve? It takes no great stretch of imagination to envisage a feather as a modified scale, basically like that of a reptile—a longish scale loosely attached, whose outer edges frayed and spread out until it evolved into the highly complex structure that it is today."[11] But do you think such an explanation is truly scientific? Or does it read more like science fiction?

[17] Consider further the design of the bird for flight. The bird's bones are thin and hollow, unlike the reptile's solid ones. Yet strength is required for flight, so inside the bird's bones there are struts, like the braces inside of airplane wings. This design of the bones serves another purpose: It helps to explain another exclusive marvel of birds—their respiratory system.

[18] Muscular wings beating for hours or even days in flight generate much heat, yet, without sweat glands for cooling, the bird copes with the problem —it has an air-cooled "engine." A system of air sacs

---

15. How do birds care for their feathers?
16. What did one evolutionist say about the origin of feathers?
17. How do the bones of a bird differ from those of a reptile?
18. What structures help birds keep cool on long flights?

The eagle's eye functions as a telescope, and the warbler's eye as a magnifying glass

reach into almost every important part of the body, even into the hollow bones, and body heat is relieved by this internal circulation of air. Also, because of these air sacs, birds extract oxygen from air much more efficiently than any other vertebrate. How is this done?

[19] In reptiles and mammals, the lungs take in and give out air, like bellows that alternately fill and empty. But in birds there is a constant flow of fresh air going through the lungs, during both inhaling and exhaling. Simply put, the system works like this: When the bird inhales, the air goes to certain

19. What enables birds to breathe thin air?

78

air sacs; these serve as bellows to push the air into the lungs. From the lungs the air goes into other air sacs, and these eventually expel it. This means that there is a stream of fresh air constantly going through the lungs in one direction, much like water flowing through a sponge. The blood in the capillaries of the lungs is flowing in the opposite direction. It is this countercurrent between air and blood that makes the bird's respiratory system exceptional. Because of it, birds can breathe the thin air of high altitudes, flying at over 20,000 feet for days on end as they migrate thousands of miles.

[20] Other features widen the gulf between bird and reptile. Eyesight is one. From eagles to warblers, there are eyes like telescopes and eyes like magnifying glasses. Birds have more sensory cells in their eyes than have any other living things. Also, the feet of birds are different. When they come down to roost, tendons automatically lock their toes around the branch. And they have only four toes instead of the reptile's five. Additionally, they have no vocal cords, but they have a syrinx out of which come melodious songs like those of the nightingales and mockingbirds. Consider too, that reptiles have a three-chambered heart; a bird's heart has four chambers. Beaks also set birds apart from reptiles: beaks that serve as nutcrackers, beaks that filter food from muddy water, beaks that hammer out holes in trees, crossbill beaks that open up pinecones—the variety seems endless. And yet the beak, with such specialized design, is said to have evolved by chance from the nose of a reptile! Does such an explanation seem credible to you?

[21] At one time evolutionists believed that *Archaeopteryx,* meaning "ancient wing" or "ancient bird," was a link between reptile and bird. But now, many do not. Its fossilized remains reveal perfectly

Archaeopteryx is **no link between reptile and bird**

---

20. What other features widen the gulf between bird and reptile?
21. What disqualifies *Archaeopteryx* as a link between reptile and bird?

The young of mammals are born alive and get milk from their mothers

formed feathers on aerodynamically designed wings capable of flight. Its wing and leg bones were thin and hollow. Its supposed reptilian features are found in birds today. And it does not predate birds, because fossils of other birds have been found in rocks of the same period as *Archaeopteryx*.[12]

The Gulf Between Reptile and Mammal

[22] Major differences leave a wide gulf between reptiles and mammals. The very name "mammal" points up one big difference: the existence of mammary glands that give milk for the young, which are born alive. Theodosius Dobzhansky suggested that these milk glands "may be modified sweat glands."[13] But reptiles do not even have sweat glands. Moreover, sweat glands give off waste products, not food. And unlike baby reptiles, the mammalian young have both the instincts and the muscles to suck the milk from their mother.

[23] Mammals have other features, also, that are not found in reptiles. Mammalian mothers have highly complex placentas for the nourishment and development of their unborn young. Reptiles do not. There is no diaphragm in reptiles, but mammals have a diaphragm that separates the thorax from the abdomen. The organ of Corti in the ears of mammals is not found in reptilian ears. This tiny complex organ has 20,000 rods and 30,000 nerve endings. Mammals maintain a constant body temperature, whereas reptiles do not.

[24] Mammals also have three bones in their ears, while reptiles have only one. Where did the two "extras" come from? Evolutionary theory attempts to explain it as follows: Reptiles have at least four bones in the lower jaw, whereas mammals have only one; so, when reptiles became mammals there

22. What difference between reptile and mammal is indicated by the very name "mammal"?
23, 24. What other features do mammals have that reptiles do not?

was supposedly a reshuffling of bones; some from the reptile's lower jaw moved to the mammal's middle ear to make the three bones there and, in the process, left only one for the mammal's lower jaw. However, the problem with this line of reasoning is that there is no fossil evidence whatsoever to support it. It is merely wishful conjecture.

25 Another problem involving bones: Reptilian legs are anchored at the side of the body so that the belly is on or very near the ground. But in mammals the legs are under the body and raise it off the ground. Regarding this difference, Dobzhansky commented: "This change, minor though it may seem, has necessitated widespread alterations of the skeleton and the musculature." He then acknowledged another major difference between reptiles and mammals: "Mammals have greatly elaborated their teeth. Instead of the simple peg-like teeth of the reptile, there is a great variety of mammalian teeth adapted for nipping, grasping, piercing, cutting, pounding, or grinding food."[14]

26 One last item: When the amphibian supposedly evolved into a reptile, the wastes eliminated were noted to have changed from urea to uric acid. But when the reptile became a mammal there was a reversal. Mammals went back to the amphibian way, eliminating wastes as urea. In effect, evolution went backward—something that theoretically it is not supposed to do.

"No more tragic mistake could be made than to consider man 'merely an animal'"

The Greatest Gulf of All

27 Physically, man fits the general definition of a mammal. However, one evolutionist stated: "No more tragic mistake could be made than to consider man 'merely an animal.' Man is unique; he differs

---

25. What further differences are there between reptiles and mammals?
26. What reversal would evolution have had to make in the elimination of wastes?
27. What did one evolutionist say would be a "tragic mistake"?

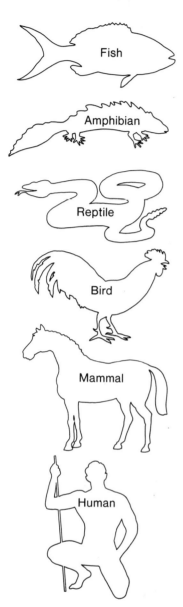

Fish

Amphibian

Reptile

Bird

Mammal

Human

"Intermediate forms are missing from the fossil record . . . because there were no intermediate forms"

from all other animals in many properties, such as speech, tradition, culture, and an enormously extended period of growth and parental care."[15]

[28] What sets man apart from all other creatures on earth is his brain. The information stored in some 100 billion neurons of the human brain would fill about 20 million volumes! The power of abstract thought and of speech sets man far apart from any animal, and the ability to record accumulating knowledge is one of man's most remarkable characteristics. Use of this knowledge has enabled him to surpass all other living kinds on earth—even to the point of going to the moon and back. Truly, as one scientist said, man's brain "is different and immeasurably more complicated than anything else in the known universe."[16]

[29] Another feature that makes the gulf between man and animal the greatest one of all is man's moral and spiritual values, which stem from such qualities as love, justice, wisdom, power, mercy. This is alluded to in Genesis when it says that man is made 'in the image and likeness of God.' And it is the gulf between man and animal that is the greatest chasm of all.—Genesis 1:26.

[30] Thus, vast differences exist between the major divisions of life. Many new structures, programmed instincts and qualities separate them. Is it reasonable to think they could have originated by means of undirected chance happenings? As we have seen, the fossil evidence does not support that view. No fossils can be found to bridge the gaps. As Hoyle and Wickramasinghe say: "Intermediate forms are missing from the fossil record. Now we see why, essentially because there were no intermediate forms."[17] For those whose ears are open to hear, the fossil record is saying: "Special creation."

28. How does man's brain set him apart from the animals?
29. What fact makes the gulf between man and animal the greatest one of all?
30. What is the fossil record really saying?

Chapter 7

"Ape-Men"—What Were They?

FOR many years there have been reports that the fossil remains of apelike humans have been found. Scientific literature abounds with artists' renderings of such creatures. Are these the evolutionary transitions between beast and man? Are "ape-men" our ancestors? Evolutionary scientists claim that they are. That is why we often read expressions such as this article title in a science magazine: "How Ape Became Man."[1]

[2] True, some evolutionists do not feel that these theoretical ancestors of man should rightly be called "apes." Even so, some of their colleagues are not so exacting.[2] Stephen Jay Gould says: "People . . . evolved from apelike ancestors."[3] And George Gaylord Simpson stated: "The common ancestor would certainly be called an ape or a monkey in popular speech by anybody who saw it. Since the terms *ape* and *monkey* are defined by popular usage, man's ancestors *were* apes or monkeys."[4]

[3] Why is the fossil record so important in the

1, 2. What does evolutionary theory assert that our ancestors were?
3. Why is the fossil record considered important in determining man's ancestry?

Since the living world does not provide any link between man and beast, evolutionists hoped that fossils would

effort to document the existence of apelike ancestors for humankind? Because today's living world has nothing in it to support the idea. As shown in Chapter 6, there is an enormous gulf between humans and any animals existing today, including the ape family. Hence, since the living world does not provide a link between man and ape, it was hoped that the fossil record would.

[4] From the standpoint of evolution, the obvious gulf between man and ape today is strange. Evolutionary theory holds that as animals progressed up the evolutionary scale, they became more capable of surviving. Why, then, is the "inferior" ape family still in existence, but not a single one of the presumed intermediate forms, which were supposed to be more advanced in evolution? Today we see chimpanzees, gorillas and orangutans, but no "ape-men." Does it seem likely that every one of the more recent and supposedly more advanced "links" between apelike creatures and modern man should have become extinct, but not the lower apes?

Why did "inferior" apes and monkeys survive, but not a single "superior" "ape-man"?

How Much Fossil Evidence?

[5] From the accounts in scientific literature, in museum displays and on television, it would seem that surely there must be abundant evidence that

4. From evolution's standpoint, why is the absence of living "ape-men" so strange?
5. What impression do the accounts leave about the fossil evidence for human evolution?

humans evolved from apelike creatures. Is this really so? For instance, what fossil evidence was there of this in Darwin's day? Was it such evidence that encouraged him to formulate his theory?

[6] *The Bulletin of the Atomic Scientists* informs us: "The early theories of human evolution are really very odd, if one stops to look at them. David Pilbeam has described the early theories as 'fossil-free.' That is, here were theories about human evolution that one would think would require some fossil evidence, but in fact there were either so few fossils that they exerted no influence on the theory, or there were no fossils at all. So between man's supposed closest relatives and the early human fossils, there was only the imagination of nineteenth century scientists." This scientific publication shows why: "People wanted to believe in evolution, human evolution, and this affected the results of their work."[5]

Early theories of human evolution were "the imagination of nineteenth century scientists"

[7] After more than a century of searching, how much fossil evidence is there of "ape-men"? Richard Leakey stated: "Those working in this field have so little evidence upon which to base their conclusions that it is necessary for them frequently to change their conclusions."[6] *New Scientist* commented: "Judged by the amount of evidence upon which it is based, the study of fossil man hardly deserves to be more than a sub-discipline of palaeontology or anthropology. . . . the collection is so tantalisingly incomplete, and the specimens themselves often so fragmentary and inconclusive."[7]

"The primary scientific evidence is a pitifully small array of bones"

[8] Similarly, the book *Origins* admits: "As we move farther along the path of evolution towards humans the going becomes distinctly uncertain, again owing to the paucity of fossil evidence."[8] *Science* magazine adds: "The primary scientific evidence is a

6. (a) Were earlier theories about human evolution based on fossil evidence? (b) Why could evolution gain acceptance without solid evidence?
7-9. How much fossil evidence for human evolution is there now?

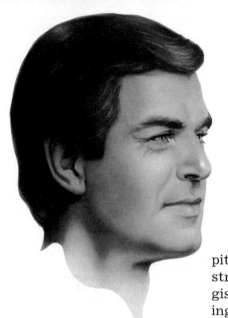

An evolutionist acknowledges: "We have no evidence for biological change in brain size or structure since *Homo sapiens* appeared in the fossil record"

pitifully small array of bones from which to construct man's evolutionary history. One anthropologist has compared the task to that of reconstructing the plot of *War and Peace* with 13 randomly selected pages."[9]

[9] Just how sparse is the fossil record regarding "ape-men"? Note the following. *Newsweek:* "'You could put all the fossils on the top of a single desk,' said Elwyn Simons of Duke University."[10] *The New York Times:* "The known fossil remains of man's ancestors would fit on a billiard table. That makes a poor platform from which to peer into the mists of the last few million years."[11] *Science Digest:* "The remarkable fact is that all the physical evidence we have for human evolution can still be placed, with room to spare, inside a single coffin! . . . Modern apes, for instance, seem to have sprung out of nowhere. They have no yesterday, no fossil record. And the true origin of modern humans—of upright, naked, toolmaking, big-brained beings—is, if we are to be honest with ourselves, an equally mysterious matter."[12]

[10] Modern-type humans, with the capacity to reason, plan, invent, build on previous knowledge and use complex languages, appear suddenly in the fossil record. Gould, in his book *The Mismeasure of Man,* notes: "We have no evidence for biological change in brain size or structure since *Homo sapi-*

10. What does the evidence show about the appearance of modern-type humans?

ens appeared in the fossil record some fifty thousand years ago."[13] Thus, the book *The Universe Within* asks: "What caused evolution . . . to produce, as if overnight, modern humankind with its highly special brain?"[14] Evolution is unable to answer. But could the answer lie in the *creation* of a very complex, different creature?

Where Are the "Links"?

[11] However, have not scientists found the necessary "links" between apelike animals and man? Not according to the evidence. *Science Digest* speaks of "the lack of a missing link to explain the relatively sudden appearance of modern man."[15] *Newsweek* observed: "The missing link between man and the apes . . . is merely the most glamorous of a whole hierarchy of phantom creatures. In the fossil record, missing links are the rule."[16]

[12] Because there are no links, "phantom creatures" have to be fabricated from minimal evidence and passed off as though they had really existed. That explains why the following contradiction could occur, as reported by a science magazine: "Humans evolved in gradual steps from their apelike ancestors and not, as some scientists contend, in sudden jumps from one form to another. . . . But other anthropologists, working with much the same data, reportedly have reached exactly the opposite conclusion."[17]

"The search for the proverbial 'missing link' . . . allows speculation and myth to flourish"

[13] Thus we can better understand the observation of respected anatomist Solly Zuckerman who wrote in the *Journal of the Royal College of Surgeons of Edinburgh:* "The search for the proverbial 'missing link' in man's evolution, that holy grail of a never dying sect of anatomists and biologists, allows speculation and myth to flourish as happily to-day as they did 50 years ago and more."[18] He noted that,

---

11. What is admittedly "the rule" in the fossil record?
12. In what has the lack of links resulted?
13. What has resulted from the inability to find "missing links"?

all too often, facts were ignored, and instead, what was currently popular was championed in spite of evidence to the contrary.

Man's "Family Tree"

[14] As a result, the "family tree" often drawn of man's claimed evolution from lower animals changes constantly. For example, Richard Leakey stated that a more recent fossil discovery "leaves in ruins the notion that all early fossils can be arranged in an orderly sequence of evolutionary change."[19] And a newspaper report regarding that discovery declared: "Every single book on anthropology, every article on the evolution of man, every drawing of man's family tree will have to be junked. They are apparently wrong."[20]

"Every drawing of man's family tree will have to be junked"

[15] The theoretical family tree of human evolution is littered with the castoffs of previously accepted "links." An editorial in *The New York Times* observed that evolutionary science "includes so much room for conjecture that theories of how man came to be tend to tell more about their author than their subject. . . . The finder of a new skull often seems to redraw the family tree of man, with his discovery on the center line that leads to man and everyone else's skulls on side lines leading nowhere."[21]

[16] In a book review of *The Myths of Human Evolution* written by evolutionists Niles Eldredge and Ian Tattersall, *Discover* magazine observed that the authors eliminated any evolutionary family tree. Why? After noting that "the links that make up the ancestry of the human species can only be guessed at," this publication stated: "Eldredge and Tattersall insist that man searches for his ancestry in vain. . . . If the evidence were there, they contend, 'one could confidently expect that as more

14, 15. What has the evidence done to the evolutionary human "family tree"?
16. Why did two scientists omit a family tree for evolution in their book?

hominid fossils were found the story of human evolution would become clearer. Whereas, if anything, the opposite has occurred.'"

[17] *Discover* concluded: "The human species, and all species, will remain orphans of a sort, the identities of their parents lost to the past."[22] Perhaps "lost" from the standpoint of evolutionary theory. But has not the Genesis alternative "found" our parents as they actually are in the fossil record —fully human, just as we are?

[18] The fossil record reveals a distinct, separate origin for apes and for humans. That is why fossil evidence of man's link to apelike beasts is nonexistent. The links really have never been there.

What Did They Look Like?

[19] However, if man's ancestors were not apelike, why do so many pictures and replicas of "ape-men" flood scientific publications and museums around the world? On what are these based? The book *The Biology of Race* answers: "The flesh and hair on such reconstructions have to be filled in by resorting to the imagination." It adds: "Skin color; the color, form, and distribution of the hair; the form of the features; and the aspect of the face—of these characters we know absolutely nothing for any prehistoric men."[23]

[20] *Science Digest* also commented: "The vast majority of artists' conceptions are based more on imagination than on evidence. . . . Artists must create something between an ape and a human being; the older the specimen is said to be, the more apelike they make it."[24] Fossil hunter Donald Johanson acknowledged: "No one can be sure just what any extinct hominid looked like."[25]

[21] Indeed, *New Scientist* reported that there is not

On what are drawings of "ape-men" based? Evolutionists answer: "the imagination," "pure fiction in most respects," "sheer invention"

17, 18. (a) How can what some evolutionists consider "lost" be "found"? (b) How does the fossil record confirm this?
19, 20. On what are drawings of "ape-men" based?
21. What, really, are the depictions of "ape-men"?

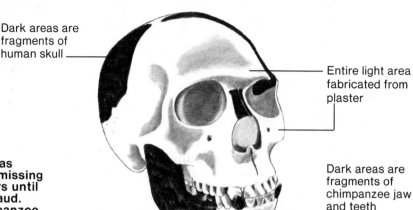

Dark areas are fragments of human skull

Entire light area fabricated from plaster

Dark areas are fragments of chimpanzee jaw and teeth

Piltdown man was accepted as a "missing link" for 40 years until exposed as a fraud. Parts of a chimpanzee jaw and teeth had been combined with parts of a human skull

There is not "enough evidence from fossil material to take our theorising out of the realms of fantasy"

"enough evidence from fossil material to take our theorising out of the realms of fantasy."[26] So the depictions of "ape-men" are, as one evolutionist admitted, "pure fiction in most respects . . . sheer invention."[27] Thus in *Man, God and Magic* Ivar Lissner commented: "Just as we are slowly learning that primitive men are not necessarily savages, so we must learn to realize that the early men of the Ice Age were neither brute beasts nor semi-apes nor cretins. Hence the ineffable stupidity of all attempts to reconstruct Neanderthal or even Peking man."[28]

[22] In their desire to find evidence of "ape-men," some scientists have been taken in by outright fraud, for example, the Piltdown man in 1912. For about 40 years it was accepted as genuine by most of the evolutionary community. Finally, in 1953, the hoax was uncovered when modern techniques revealed that human and ape bones had been put together and artificially aged. In another instance, an apelike "missing link" was drawn up and presented in the press. But it was later acknowledged that the "evidence" consisted of only one tooth that belonged to an extinct form of pig.[29]

What Were They?

[23] If "ape-man" reconstructions are not valid, then what were those ancient creatures whose fossil

22. How have many supporters of evolution been deceived?
23. What really were some fossils that had been presumed to be ancestors of man?

90

bones have been found? One of these earliest mammals claimed to be in the line of man is a small, rodentlike animal said to have lived about 70 million years ago. In their book *Lucy: The Beginnings of Humankind,* Donald Johanson and Maitland Edey wrote: "They were insect-eating quadrupeds about the size and shape of squirrels."[30] Richard Leakey called the mammal a "rat-like primate."[31] But is there any solid evidence that these tiny animals were the ancestors of humans? No, instead only wishful speculation. No transitional stages have ever linked them with anything except what they were: small, rodentlike mammals.

A shrewlike rodent is said to be an ancestor of man. But there is no fossil evidence of such a relationship

[24] Next on the generally accepted list, with an admitted gap of about 40 million years, are fossils found in Egypt and named *Aegyptopithecus* —Egypt ape. This creature is said to have lived about 30 million years ago. Magazines, newspapers and books have displayed pictures of this small creature with headings such as: "Monkey-like creature was our ancestor." (*Time*)[32] "Monkeylike African Primate Called Common Ancestor of Man and Apes." (*The New York Times*)[33] "*Aegyptopithecus* is an ancestor which we share with living apes." (*Origins*)[34] But where are the links between it and the rodent before it? Where are the links to what is placed after it in the evolutionary lineup? None have been found.

This monkeylike creature has been called one of our ancestors. No fossil evidence exists for this claim

The Rise and Fall of "Ape–Men"

[25] Following another admittedly gigantic gap in the fossil record, another fossil creature had been presented as the first humanlike ape. It was said to have lived about 14 million years ago and was called *Ramapithecus*—Rama's ape (Rama was a mythical prince of India). Fossils of it were found

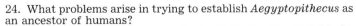

24. What problems arise in trying to establish *Aegyptopithecus* as an ancestor of humans?
25, 26. (a) What claim was made about *Ramapithecus?* (b) On what fossil evidence was it reconstructed so as to appear as an "ape-man"?

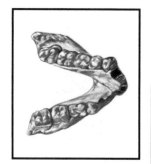

Based on just teeth and parts of jawbones, *Ramapithecus* was called "the first representative of the human family." Further evidence showed that it was not

in India about half a century ago. From these fossils was constructed an apelike creature, upright, on two limbs. Of it *Origins* stated: "As far as one can say at the moment, it is the first representative of the human family."[35]

[26] What was the fossil evidence for this conclusion? The same publication remarked: "The evidence concerning *Ramapithecus* is considerable —though in absolute terms it remains tantalizingly small: fragments of upper and lower jaws, plus a collection of teeth."[36] Do you think that this was "considerable" enough "evidence" to reconstruct an upright "ape-man" ancestor of humans? Yet, this mostly hypothetical creature was drawn by artists as an "ape-man," and pictures of it flooded evolutionary literature—all on the basis of jawbone fragments and teeth! Still, as *The New York Times* reported, for decades *Ramapithecus* "sat as securely as anything can at the base of the human evolutionary tree."[37]

[27] However, that is no longer the case. Recent and more complete fossil finds revealed that *Ramapithecus* closely resembled the present-day ape family. So *New Scientist* now declares: "*Ramapithecus* cannot have been the first member of the human line."[38] Such new information provoked the following question in *Natural History* magazine: "How

27. Later evidence proved what regarding *Ramapithecus*?

did *Ramapithecus,* . . . reconstructed only from teeth and jaws—without a known pelvis, limb bones, or skull—sneak into this manward-marching procession?"[39] Obviously, a great deal of wishful thinking must have gone into such an effort to make the evidence say what it does not say.

[28] Another gap of vast proportions lies between that creature and the next one that had been listed as an "ape-man" ancestor. This is called *Australopithecus*—southern ape. Fossils of it were first found in southern Africa in the 1920's. It had a small apelike braincase, heavy jawbone and was pictured as walking on two limbs, stooped over, hairy and apish looking. It was said to have lived beginning about three or four million years ago. In time it came to be accepted by nearly all evolutionists as man's ancestor.

[29] For instance, the book *The Social Contract* noted: "With one or two exceptions all competent investigators in this field now agree that the australopithecines . . . are actual human ancestors."[40] *The New York Times* declared: "It was *Australopithecus* . . . that eventually evolved into *Homo sapiens,* or modern man."[41] And in *Man, Time, and Fossils* Ruth Moore said: "By all the evidence men at last had met their long unknown, early ancestors." Emphatically she declared: "The evidence was overwhelming . . . the missing link had at long last been found."[42]

[30] But when the evidence for anything actually is flimsy or nonexistent, or based on outright deception, sooner or later the claim comes to nothing. This has proved to be the case with many past examples of presumed "ape-men."

[31] So, too, with *Australopithecus*. More research has disclosed that its skull "differed from that of

"*Ramapithecus* cannot have been the first member of the human line"

28, 29. What claim was made for *Australopithecus?*
30, 31. What does later evidence show regarding *Australopithecus?*

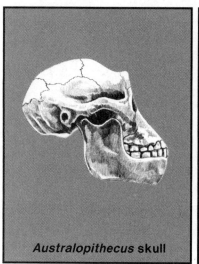

Australopithecus skull

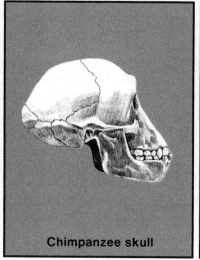

Chimpanzee skull

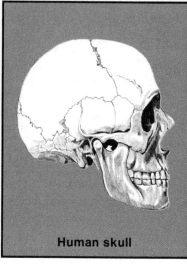

Human skull

At one time *Australopithecus* was accepted as a human ancestor, "the missing link." Now some scientists agree that its skull was "overwhelmingly simian [ape]—not human"

humans in more ways than its smaller brain capacity."[43] Anatomist Zuckerman wrote: "When compared with human and simian [ape] skulls, the Australopithecine skull is in appearance overwhelmingly simian—not human. The contrary proposition could be equated to an assertion that black is white."[44] He also said: "Our findings leave little doubt that . . . *Australopithecus* resembles not *Homo sapiens* but the living monkeys and apes."[45] Donald Johanson also said: "Australopithecines . . . were *not* men."[46] Similarly Richard Leakey called it "unlikely that our direct ancestors are evolutionary descendants of the australopithecines."[47]

[32] If any australopithecines were found alive today, they would be put in zoos with other apes. No one would call them "ape-men." The same is true of other fossil "cousins" that resemble it, such as a smaller type of australopithecine called "Lucy." Of it Robert Jastrow says: "This brain was not large in absolute size; it was a third the size of a human brain."[48] Obviously, it too was simply an "ape." In fact, *New Scientist* said that "Lucy" had a skull "very like a chimpanzee's."[49]

---

32. If such creatures were still living today, how would they be regarded?

33 Another fossil type is called *Homo erectus*—upright man. Its brain size and shape do fall into the lower range of modern man's. Also, the *Encyclopœdia Britannica* observed that "the limb bones thus far discovered have been indistinguishable from those of *H[omo] sapiens.*"[50] However, it is unclear whether it was human or not. If so, then it was merely a branch of the human family and died off.

The Human Family

34 Neanderthal man (named after the Neander district in Germany where the first fossil was found) was undoubtedly human. At first he was pictured as bent over, stupid looking, hairy and apelike. Now it is known that this mistaken reconstruction was based on a fossil skeleton badly deformed by disease. Since then, many Neanderthal fossils have been found, confirming that he was not much different from modern humans. In his book *Ice,* Fred Hoyle stated: "There is no evidence that Neanderthal man was in any way inferior to ourselves."[51] As a result, recent drawings of Neanderthals have taken on a more modern look.

"There is no evidence that Neanderthal man was in any way inferior to ourselves"

35 Another fossil type frequently encountered in scientific literature is Cro-Magnon man. It was named for the locality in southern France where his bones were first unearthed. These specimens "were so virtually indistinguishable from those of today that even the most skeptical had to concede that they were humans," said the book *Lucy.*[52]

36 Thus, the evidence is clear that belief in "apemen" is unfounded. Instead, humans have all the earmarks of being created—separate and distinct from any animal. Humans reproduce only after their own kind. They do so today and have always

33. What fossil type may or may not have been human?
34. How have ideas changed about Neanderthal man?
35. What were Cro-Magnon types?
36. What are the facts regarding apelike fossils of the past, and humanlike fossils?

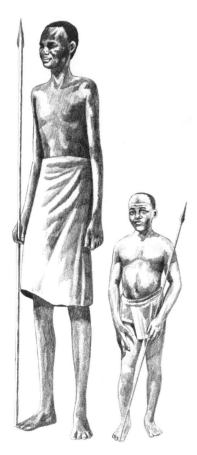

As is the case in the fossil record, today there is great variety in size and shape of bone structure in humans. But all belong to the human "kind"

done so in the past. Any apelike creatures that lived in the past were just that—apes, or monkeys—not humans. And fossils of ancient humans that differ slightly from humans of today simply demonstrate variety within the human family, just as today we have many varieties living side by side. There are seven-foot humans and there are pygmies, with varying sizes and shapes of skeletons. But all belong to the same human "kind," not animal "kind."

What About the Dates?

[37] Biblical chronology indicates that a period of about 6,000 years has passed since the creation of humans. Why, then, does one often read about far longer periods of time since acknowledged human types of fossils appeared?

[38] Before concluding that Bible chronology is in error, consider that radioactive dating methods have come under sharp criticism by some scientists. A scientific journal reported on studies showing that "dates determined by radioactive decay may be off—not only by a few years, but by orders of magnitude." It said: "Man, instead of having walked the earth for 3.6 million years, may have been around for only a few thousand."[53]

[39] For example, the radiocarbon "clock." This method of radiocarbon dating was developed over a period of two decades by scientists all over the world. It was widely acclaimed for accurate dating of artifacts from man's ancient history. But then a conference of the world's experts, including radiochemists, archaeologists and geologists, was held in Uppsala, Sweden, to compare notes. The report of their conference showed that the fundamental assumptions on which the measurements were

37. Biblical chronology indicates that humans have been on earth for how long?
38. Do dates that are determined by radioactive decay and that are in conflict with Bible chronology prove that the Bible is in error?
39. Is the radiocarbon "clock" always reliable?

Humans have all the earmarks of being created separate and distinct from the apes

based had been found untrustworthy to a greater or lesser degree. For example, it found that the rate of radioactive carbon formation in the atmosphere has not been consistent in the past and that this method is not reliable in dating objects from about 2,000 B.C.E. or before.[54]

40 Keep in mind that truly reliable evidence of man's activity on earth is given, not in millions of years, but in thousands. For example, in *The Fate of the Earth* we read: "Only six or seven thousand years ago . . . civilization emerged, enabling us to build up a human world."[55] *The Last Two Million Years* states: "In the Old World, most of the critical

---

40. How do historical records support Bible chronology as to the age of the human race?

steps in the farming revolution were taken between 10,000 and 5000 BC." It also says: "Only for the last 5000 years has man left written records."[56] The fact that the fossil record shows modern man suddenly appearing on earth, and that reliable historical records are admittedly recent, harmonizes with the Bible's chronology for human life on earth.

[41] In this regard, note what Nobel prize winning nuclear physicist W. F. Libby, one of the pioneers in radiocarbon dating, stated in *Science:* "The research in the development of the dating technique consisted of two stages—dating of samples from the historical and the prehistorical epochs, respectively. Arnold [a co-worker] and I had our first shock when our advisers informed us that history extended back only for 5000 years. . . . You read statements to the effect that such and such a society or archeological site is 20,000 years old. We learned rather abruptly that these numbers, these ancient ages, are not known accurately."[57]

[42] When reviewing a book on evolution, English author Malcolm Muggeridge commented on the lack of evidence for evolution. He noted that wild speculations flourished nevertheless. Then he said: "The Genesis account seems, by comparison, sober enough and at least has the merit of being validly related to what we know about human beings and their behavior." He said that the unfounded claims of millions of years for man's evolution "and wild leaps from skull to skull, cannot but strike anyone not caught up in the [evolutionary] myth as pure fantasy." Muggeridge concluded: "Posterity will surely be amazed, and I hope vastly amused, that such slipshod and unconvincing theorizing should have so easily captivated twentieth-century minds and been so widely and recklessly applied."[58]

"Posterity will surely be amazed . . . that such slipshod and unconvincing theorizing should have so easily captivated twentieth-century minds"

41. What did a pioneer in the field of radiocarbon dating say regarding "prehistorical" dates?
42. What did an English author comment about the difference between evolutionary accounts and the Genesis account?

Chapter 8

Mutations—
A Basis for Evolution?

THERE is another difficulty facing the theory of evolution. Just *how* is it supposed to have happened? What is a basic mechanism that is presumed to have enabled one type of living thing to evolve into another type? Evolutionists say that various changes inside the nucleus of the cell play their part. And foremost among these are the "accidental" changes known as *mutations*. It is believed that the particular parts involved in these mutational changes are the genes and chromosomes in sex cells, since mutations in them can be passed along to one's descendants.

[2] "Mutations . . . are the basis of evolution," states *The World Book Encyclopedia*.[1] Similarly, paleontologist Steven Stanley called mutations "the raw materials" for evolution.[2] And geneticist Peo Koller declared that mutations "are necessary for evolutionary progress."[3]

[3] However, it is not just any kind of mutation that evolution requires. Robert Jastrow pointed to the need for "a slow accumulation of favorable mutations."[4] And Carl Sagan added: "Mutations —sudden changes in heredity—breed true. They provide the raw material of evolution. The environment selects those few mutations that enhance survival, resulting in a series of slow transformations of one lifeform into another, the origin of new species."[5]

"Mutations . . . are the basis of evolution"

1, 2. What mechanism is said to be a basis for evolution?
3. What type of mutations would be required for evolution?

99

4 It also has been said that mutations may be a key to the rapid change called for by the "punctuated equilibrium" theory. Writing in *Science Digest,* John Gliedman stated: "Evolutionary revisionists believe mutations in key regulatory genes may be just the genetic jackhammers their quantum-leap theory requires." However, British zoologist Colin Patterson observed: "Speculation is free. We know nothing about these regulatory master genes."[6] But aside from such speculations, it is generally accepted that the mutations supposedly involved in evolution are small accidental changes that accumulate over a long period of time.

5 How do mutations originate? It is thought that most of them occur in the normal process of cell reproduction. But experiments have shown that they also can be caused by external agents such as radiation and chemicals. And how often do they happen? The reproduction of genetic material in the cell is remarkably consistent. Relatively speaking, considering the number of cells that divide in a living thing, mutations do not occur very often. As the *Encyclopedia Americana* commented, the reproducing "of the DNA chains composing a gene is remarkably accurate. Misprints or miscopying are infrequent accidents."[7]

Mutations are likened to "accidents" in the genetic machinery. But accidents cause harm, not good

Are They Helpful or Harmful?

6 If beneficial mutations are a basis of evolution, what proportion of them are beneficial? There is overwhelming agreement on this point among evolutionists. For example, Carl Sagan declares: "Most of them are harmful or lethal."[8] Peo Koller states: "The greatest proportion of mutations are deleterious to the individual who carries the mutated gene. It was found in experiments that, for every suc-

4. What difficulty arises with the claim that mutations may be involved in rapid evolutionary changes?
5. How do mutations originate?
6, 7. What proportion of mutations are harmful rather than beneficial?

cessful or useful mutation, there are many thousands which are harmful."[9]

[7] Excluding any "neutral" mutations, then, harmful ones outnumber those that are supposedly beneficial by thousands to one. "Such results are to be expected of accidental changes occurring in any complicated organization," states the *Encyclopædia Britannica*.[10] That is why mutations are said to be responsible for hundreds of diseases that are genetically determined.[11]

[8] Because of the harmful nature of mutations, the *Encyclopedia Americana* acknowledged: "The fact that most mutations are damaging to the organism seems hard to reconcile with the view that mutation is the source of raw materials for evolution. Indeed, mutants illustrated in biology textbooks are a collection of freaks and monstrosities and mutation seems to be a destructive rather than a constructive process."[12] When mutated insects were placed in competition with normal ones, the result was always the same. As G. Ledyard Stebbins observed: "After a greater or lesser number of generations the mutants are eliminated."[13] They could not compete because they were not improved but were degenerate and at a disadvantage.

[9] In his book *The Wellsprings of Life,* science writer Isaac Asimov admitted: "Most mutations are for the worse." However, he then asserted: "In the long run, to be sure, mutations make the course of evolution move onward and upward."[14] But do they? Would any process that resulted in harm more than 999 times out of 1,000 be considered beneficial? If you wanted a house built, would you hire a builder who, for every correct piece of work, turned out thousands that were defective? If a driver of an automobile made thousands of bad decisions for every good one when driving, would you want to

"Mutation seems to be a destructive rather than a constructive process"

---

8. How do actual results verify an encyclopedia's observation?
9, 10. Why is it an unwarranted assumption that mutations account for evolution?

If a builder turned out thousands of bad pieces of work for every good one, would you hire him?

If a driver made thousands of bad decisions for every good one, would you ride with him?

If a surgeon made thousands of wrong moves for every right one, would you let him operate on you?

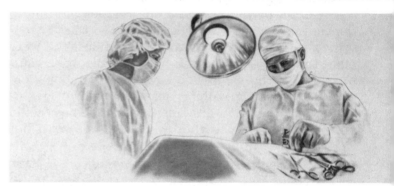

ride with him? If a surgeon made thousands of wrong moves for every right one when operating, would you want him to operate on you?

[10] Geneticist Dobzhansky once said: "An accident, a random change, in any delicate mechanism can hardly be expected to improve it. Poking a stick into the machinery of one's watch or one's radio set will seldom make it work better."[15] Thus, ask yourself: Does it seem reasonable that all the amazingly complex cells, organs, limbs and processes that exist in living things were *built up* by a procedure that *tears down?*

Do Mutations Produce Anything New?

Dobzhansky: "Poking a stick into . . . one's radio set will seldom make it work better"

[11] Even if all mutations were beneficial, could they produce anything new? No, they could not. A mutation could only result in a variation of a trait that is already there. It provides variety, but never anything new.

[12] *The World Book Encyclopedia* gives an example of what might happen with a beneficial mutation: "A plant in a dry area might have a mutant gene that causes it to grow larger and stronger roots. The plant would have a better chance of survival than others of its species because its roots could absorb more water."[16] But has anything new appeared? No, it is still the same plant. It is not evolving into something else.

[13] Mutations may change the color or texture of a person's hair. But the hair will always be hair. It will never turn into feathers. A person's hand may be changed by mutations. It may have fingers that are abnormal. At times there may even be a hand with six fingers or with some other malformation. But it is always a hand. It never changes into something else. Nothing new is coming into existence, nor can it ever.

11-13. Do mutations ever produce anything new?

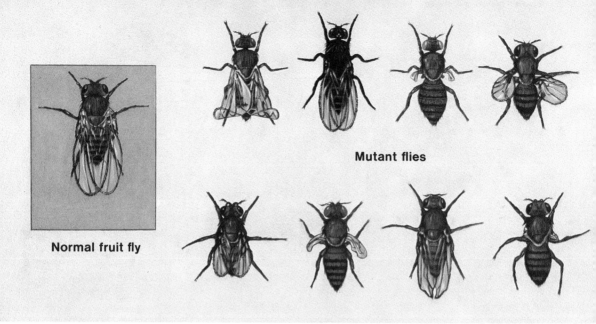

Normal fruit fly

Mutant flies

Experiments with fruit flies produced many malformed mutants, but they always remained fruit flies

The Fruit Fly Experiments

14 Few mutation experiments can equal the extensive ones conducted on the common fruit fly, *Drosophila melanogaster*. Since the early 1900's, scientists have exposed millions of these flies to X rays. This increased the frequency of mutations to more than a hundred times what was normal.

15 After all those decades, what did the experiments show? Dobzhansky revealed one result: "The clear-cut mutants of *Drosophila,* with which so much of the classical research in genetics was done, are almost without exception inferior to wild-type flies in viability, fertility, longevity."[17] Another result was that the mutations never produced anything new. The fruit flies had malformed wings, legs and bodies, and other distortions, but they always remained fruit flies. And when mutated flies were mated with each other, it was found that after a number of generations, some normal fruit flies began to hatch. If left in their natural state, these normal flies would eventually have been the survivors over the weaker mutants, preserving the fruit fly in the form in which it had originally existed.

14, 15. What have decades of experiments on fruit flies revealed?

104

[16] The hereditary code, the DNA, has a remarkable ability to repair genetic damage to itself. This helps to preserve the kind of organism it is coded for. *Scientific American* relates how "the life of every organism and its continuity from generation to generation" are preserved "by enzymes that continually repair" genetic damage. The journal states: "In particular, significant damage to DNA molecules can induce an emergency response in which increased quantities of the repair enzymes are synthesized."[18]

[17] Thus, in the book *Darwin Retried* the author relates the following about the respected geneticist, the late Richard Goldschmidt: "After observing mutations in fruit flies for many years, Goldschmidt fell into despair. The changes, he lamented, were so hopelessly micro [small] that if a thousand mutations were combined in one specimen, there would still be no new species."[19]

"If a thousand mutations were combined in one specimen, there would still be no new species"

The Peppered Moth

[18] Often in evolutionary literature England's peppered moth is referred to as a modern example of evolution in progress. *The International Wildlife Encyclopedia* stated: "This is the most striking evolutionary change ever to have been witnessed by man."[20] After observing that Darwin was plagued by his inability to demonstrate the evolution of even one species, Jastrow, in his book *Red Giants and White Dwarfs,* added: "Had he known it, an example was at hand which would have provided him with the proof he needed. The case was an exceedingly rare one."[21] The case was, of course, the peppered moth.

[19] Just what happened to the peppered moth? At first, the lighter form of this moth was more common than the darker form. This lighter type blend-

16. How does the hereditary code help to preserve organisms?
17. Why was Goldschmidt disappointed in mutation experiments?
18, 19. What claim is made for the peppered moth, and why?

Change in coloration of the peppered moth is not evolution but merely variety within a basic kind

ed well into the lighter-colored trunks of trees and so was more protected from birds. But then, because of years of pollution from industrial areas, tree trunks became darkened. Now the moths' lighter color worked against them, as birds could pick them out faster and eat them. Consequently the darker variety of peppered moth, which is said to be a mutant, survived better because it was difficult for birds to see them against the soot-darkened trees. The darker variety rapidly became the dominant type.

[20] But was the peppered moth evolving into some other type of insect? No, it was still exactly the same peppered moth, merely having a different coloration. Hence, the English medical journal *On Call*

20. How did an English medical journal explain that the peppered moth was not evolving?

referred to using this example to try to prove evolution as "notorious." It declared: "This is an excellent demonstration of the function of camouflage, but, since it begins and ends with moths and no new species is formed, it is quite irrelevant as evidence for evolution."[22]

[21] The inaccurate claim that the peppered moth is evolving is similar to several other examples. For instance, since some germs have proved resistant to antibiotics, it is claimed that evolution is taking place. But the hardier germs are still the same type, not evolving into anything else. And it is even acknowledged that the change may have been due, not to mutations, but to the fact that some germs were immune to begin with. When the others were killed off by drugs, the immune ones multiplied and became dominant. As *Evolution From Space* says: "We doubt, however, that anything more is involved in these cases than the selection of already existing genes."[23]

[22] The same process may also have been the case with some insects being immune to poisons used against them. Either the poisons killed those insects on which they were used, or they were ineffective. Those killed could not develop a resistance, since they were dead. The survival of others could mean that they had been immune at the start. Such immunity is a genetic factor that appears in some insects but not in others. In any event, the insects remained of the same kind. They were not evolving into something else.

"It is quite irrelevant as evidence for evolution"

The message confirmed by mutations is this: Living things reproduce only "according to their kinds"

"According to Their Kinds"

[23] The message once again confirmed by mutations is the formula of Genesis chapter 1: Living things reproduce only "according to their kinds."

21. What can be said about the claimed ability of germs to grow resistant to antibiotics?
22. Does the fact that some insects prove immune to poisons mean that they are evolving?
23. What Genesis standard has been confirmed also by mutations?

107

The dog family has many varieties, but dogs always remain dogs

"Breeding procedures ... would seem to refute, rather than support evolution"

The reason is that the genetic code stops a plant or an animal from moving too far from the average. There can be great variety (as can be seen, for example, among humans, cats or dogs) but not so much that one living thing could change into another. Every experiment ever conducted with mutations proves this. Also proved is the law of biogenesis, that life comes only from preexisting life, and that the parent organism and its offspring are of the same "kind."

[24] Breeding experiments also confirm this. Scientists have tried to keep changing various animals and plants indefinitely by crossbreeding. They wanted to see if, in time, they could develop new forms of life. With what result? *On Call* reports: "Breeders usually find that after a few generations, an optimum is reached beyond which further improvement is impossible, and there has been no new species formed . . . Breeding procedures, therefore, would seem to refute, rather than support evolution."[24]

---

24. How have breeding experiments shown that living things reproduce only "according to their kinds"?

108

25 Much the same observation is made in *Science* magazine: "Species do indeed have a capacity to undergo minor modifications in their physical and other characteristics, but this is limited and with a longer perspective it is reflected in an oscillation about a mean [average]."[25] So, then, what is inherited by living things is not the possibility of continued change but instead (1) stability and (2) limited ranges of variation.

26 Thus, the book *Molecules to Living Cells* states: "The cells from a carrot or from the liver of a mouse consistently retain their respective tissue and organism identities after countless cycles of reproduction."[26] And *Symbiosis in Cell Evolution* says: "All life . . . reproduces with incredible fidelity."[27] *Scientific American* also observes: "Living things are enormously diverse in form, but form is remarkably constant within any given line of descent: pigs remain pigs and oak trees remain oak trees generation after generation."[28] And a science writer commented: "Rose bushes always blossom

There is great variety in the human family, but humans reproduce only 'after their kind'

"Pigs remain pigs and oak trees remain oak trees generation after generation"

25, 26. What do scientific publications say about the limits of reproduction in living things?

into roses, never into camellias. And goats give birth to kids, never to lambs." He concluded that mutations "cannot account for overall evolution—why there are fish, reptiles, birds, and mammals."[29]

[27] The matter of variation within a kind explains something that influenced Darwin's original thinking about evolution. When he was on the Galápagos Islands he observed a type of bird called a finch. These birds were the same type as their parent kind on the South American continent, from where they apparently had migrated. But there were curious differences, such as in the shape of their beaks. Darwin interpreted this as evolution in progress. But actually it was nothing more than another example of variety within a kind, allowed for by a creature's genetic makeup. The finches were still finches. They were not turning into something else, and they never would.

[28] Thus, what Genesis says is in full harmony with scientific fact. When you plant seeds, they produce only "according to their kinds," so you can plant a garden with confidence in the dependability of that law. When cats give birth, their offspring are always cats. When humans become parents, their children are always humans. There is variation in color, size and shape, but always within the limits of the kind. Have you ever personally seen a case that was otherwise? Neither has anyone else.

Not a Basis for Evolution

[29] The conclusion is clear. No amount of accidental genetic change can cause one kind of life to turn into another kind. As French biologist Jean Rostand once said: "No, decidedly, I cannot make myself think that these 'slips' of heredity have been

Mutations "cannot account for overall evolution"

"It strikes me as a lunatic sort of logic, and I think we should be able to do better"

---

27. What did Darwin misinterpret about finches in the Galápagos Islands?
28. How can it be said, then, that scientific fact is in full harmony with the Genesis rule, "according to their kinds"?
29. What did a French biologist say about mutations?

110

The finches Darwin observed in the Galápagos always remain finches; so what he observed was variety, not evolution

able, even with the cooperation of natural selection, even with the advantage of the immense periods of time in which evolution works on life, to build the entire world, with its structural prodigality and refinements, its astounding 'adaptations.'"[30]

[30] Similarly, geneticist C. H. Waddington stated regarding the belief in mutations: "This is really the theory that if you start with any fourteen lines of coherent English and change it one letter at a time, keeping only those things that still make sense, you will eventually finish up with one of the sonnets of Shakespeare. . . . it strikes me as a lunatic sort of logic, and I think we should be able to do better."[31]

[31] The truth is as Professor John Moore declared: "Upon rigorous examination and analysis, any dogmatic assertion . . . that gene mutations are the raw material for any evolutionary process involving natural selection is an utterance of a myth."[32]

30. What comment did a geneticist make about mutations?
31. What did a scientist call the belief that mutations are the raw material for evolution?

Which Fits the Facts?

After reading the previous chapters, it is appropriate to ask: Which fits the facts, evolution or creation? The columns below show the evolution model, the creation model and the facts as found in the real world.

Predictions of Evolution Model	Predictions of Creation Model	Facts as Found in the Real World
Life evolved from nonlife by chance chemical evolution (spontaneous generation)	Life comes only from previous life; originally created by an intelligent Creator	(1) Life comes only from previous life; (2) no way to form complex genetic code by chance
Fossils should show: (1) simple life forms originating gradually; (2) transitional forms linking previous ones	Fossils should show: (1) complex forms suddenly appearing in great variety; (2) gaps separating major kinds; no linking forms	Fossils show: (1) sudden appearance of complex life in great variety; (2) each new kind separate from previous kinds; no linking forms
New kinds arising gradually; beginnings of incomplete bones and organs in various transitional stages	No new kinds gradually appearing; no incomplete bones or organs, but all parts completely formed	No new kinds gradually appearing, although many varieties; no incompletely formed bones or organs
Mutations: net result beneficial; generate new features	Mutations harmful to complex life; do not result in anything new	Small mutations harmful, large ones lethal; never result in anything new
Origin of civilization gradual, arising out of crude, brutish beginnings	Civilization contemporaneous with man; complex to begin with	Civilization appears with man; any cave dwellers were contemporary with civilization
Language evolved from simple animal sounds into complex modern languages	Language contemporaneous with man; ancient languages complex and complete	Language contemporaneous with man; ancient ones often more complex than modern
Appearance of man millions of years ago	Appearance of man about 6,000 years ago	Oldest written records date back only about 5,000 years

..The Logical Conclusion

When we compare what has been found in the real world to what evolution predicted, and to what creation predicted, is it not apparent which model fits the facts and which one conflicts with them? The evidence from the world of living things around us, and from the fossil record of things that lived long ago, testifies to the same conclusion: Life was created; it did not evolve.

No, life did not get its start in some unknown primeval "soup." Humans did not get here by way of apelike ancestors. Instead, living things were created in abundance as distinct family types. Each could multiply in great variety within its own "kind," but could not cross the boundary separating different kinds. That boundary, as can be clearly observed in living things, is enforced by sterility. And the distinction between kinds is protected by each one's unique genetic machinery.

However, there is much more that testifies to a Creator than just the facts fitting the predictions of the creation model. Consider the amazing designs and complexities that are found on the earth, indeed, throughout the universe. These, too, testify to the existence of a Supreme Intelligence. Just a few of these marvels, from the awesome universe down to the intricate designs in the microscopic world, will now be the focus of our attention in the following several chapters.

Chapter 9

Our Awesome Universe

FOR thousands of years, people have marveled at the starry heavens. On a clear night, the beautiful stars hang like shining jewels against the darkness of space. A moonlit night bathes the earth with a beauty all its own.

[2] Those who think about what they see often wonder: 'Just what is out there in space? How is it organized? Can we find out how it all got started?' Answers to these questions would no doubt help determine more accurately why the earth with its human and other life came to be, and what the future may hold.

What man is now learning about the universe has "left him stunned"

[3] Many centuries ago, it was thought that the universe was made up of the few thousand stars that could be seen with the unaided eye. But now, with powerful instruments that scan the heavens, scientists know that there is much, much more. In fact, what has been observed is far more awesome than anyone had ever imagined. The human mind is staggered by the immensity and complexity of it all. As *National Geographic* magazine commented,

1, 2. (a) How can the material heavens be described? (b) What questions do thinking people ask, and what can the answers help determine?
3. What is one result of the increasing knowledge of the universe?

A typical spiral galaxy

what man is now learning about the universe has "left him stunned."[1]

Awesome Size

[4] In recent centuries astronomers who scanned the heavens with early telescopes noticed some fuzzy, cloudlike formations. They assumed that these were nearby clouds of gases. But in the 1920's, as larger, more powerful telescopes came into use, these "gases" were found to be something far more immense and significant: galaxies.

[5] A galaxy is a vast group of stars, gas and other material rotating around a central nucleus. Galaxies have been called island universes, for each one of them is in itself like a universe. For example, consider the galaxy we live in, which is called the Milky Way. Our solar system, that is the sun and the earth and other planets with their moons, is

4. What was discovered in the 1920's?
5. (a) What is a galaxy? (b) What does our Milky Way galaxy include?

part of this galaxy. But it is only a very tiny part, for our Milky Way galaxy contains over 100 billion stars! Some scientists estimate at least 200 to 400 billion. And one science editor even stated: "There could be as many as five to ten trillion stars in the Milky Way galaxy."[2]

Our solar system, in square above, is dwarfed when compared with our Milky Way galaxy

6 The diameter of our galaxy spans so vast a distance that if you could travel as fast as the speed of light (186,282 miles *a second*) it would take you 100,000 *years* to cross it! How many miles is that? Well, since light travels about six trillion (6,000,-000,000,000) miles in a year, multiply that by 100,-000 and you have the answer: our Milky Way galaxy is about 600 quadrillion (600,000,000,000,-000,000) miles in diameter! The average distance between stars within the galaxy is said to be about six light-years, or about 36 trillion miles.

Our Milky Way galaxy contains over 100 billion stars

7 It is almost impossible for the human mind to

---

6. How vast is the distance across our galaxy?
7. What estimates have been made of the number of galaxies in the universe?

comprehend such size and distance. And yet, our galaxy is just the *beginning* of what is in outer space! There is something even more staggering. It is this: So many galaxies have now been detected that it has been said they "are as common as blades of grass in a meadow."[3] About ten billion galaxies are in the observable universe! But there are many more beyond the range of today's telescopes. Some astronomers estimate that there are 100 billion galaxies in the universe! And each galaxy may contain hundreds of billions of stars!

Clusters of Galaxies

[8] Yet, there is more. These awesome galaxies are not scattered haphazardly in space. Instead, they are usually arranged in definite groups called clusters, like grapes in a bunch. Thousands of these galactic clusters already have been observed and photographed.

[9] Some clusters contain relatively few galaxies. Our Milky Way galaxy, for example, is part of a cluster of about twenty galaxies. Within this local group, there is one "neighbor" galaxy that can be seen without a telescope on a clear night. It is the Andromeda galaxy, which has a spiral shape similar to ours.

Galaxies are arranged
in clusters, like grapes
in a bunch

[10] Other galactic clusters are made up of many dozens, perhaps hundreds or even thousands, of galaxies. One such cluster is thought to contain about 10,000 galaxies! The distance between galaxies *within* a cluster may average about a million light-years. However, the distance from one galactic cluster to another may be a hundred times that.

8. How are galaxies arranged?
9. What is included in our local galactic cluster?
10. (a) How many galaxies may be in a cluster? (b) What are the distances between galaxies, and between clusters of galaxies?

118

The planets of our solar system orbit the sun with great precision

And there is even evidence that the clusters themselves are arranged in "superclusters," like bunches of grapes on a vine. What colossal size and brilliant organization!

Similar Organization

[11] Coming down to our solar system, we find another superbly organized arrangement. The sun, which is a medium-sized star, is the "nucleus" around which the earth and the other planets with their moons move in precise orbits. Year after year, they revolve with such mathematical certainty that astronomers can accurately predict where they will be at any future time.

---

11. What similar organization do we find in our solar system?

120

¹² Looking into infinitesimal things—atoms—we see that the same precision exists. An atom is a marvel of order, resembling the order of the solar system. It includes a nucleus containing particles called protons and neutrons, surrounded by tiny orbiting electrons. All matter is made up of these building blocks. What makes one substance differ from the other is the number of protons and neutrons in the nucleus and the number and arrange-

The order in an atom resembles that of the solar system

---

12. How are atoms organized?

121

A precision watch is the product of an intelligent designer. Is not the far greater precision in the universe the product of a superior, intelligent designer?

ment of the electrons revolving around it. This has an exquisite order, since all the elements that make up matter can be arranged in exact sequence by the number of those building blocks present.

What Is Behind This Organization?

[13] As we have noted, the size of the universe is truly awesome. So is its marvelous arrangement. From the infinitely large to the infinitesimally small, from galactic clusters to atoms, the universe is characterized by superb organization. *Discover* magazine stated: "We perceived the order in surprise, and our cosmologists and physicists continue to find new and astonishing aspects of the order. . . . We used to say it was a miracle, and we still permit ourselves to refer to the whole universe as a marvel."[4] This orderly structure is acknowledged even in the word commonly used in astronomy to describe the universe—"cosmos." It is defined in one dictionary as "an orderly harmonious systematic universe."[5]

Scientists "continue to find new and astonishing aspects of the order"

[14] Former astronaut John Glenn noted "the *orderliness* of the whole universe about us," and that the galaxies were "all traveling in prescribed orbits in relation to one another." He therefore asked:

---

13. What characteristic is seen in the entire universe?
14. What comment did a former astronaut make?

122

"Could this have just happened? Was it an accident that a bunch of flotsam and jetsam suddenly started making these orbits of its own accord?" He concluded: "I can't believe that. . . . Some Power put all this into orbit and keeps it there."[6]

[15] Indeed, the universe is so precisely organized that man can use the heavenly bodies as the basis for his timekeeping. But any well-designed timepiece obviously is the product of an orderly mind that has the ability to design. An orderly mind that designs can be possessed only by an intelligent person. Then what about the far more complex design and dependability that exists throughout the universe? Would this not also betoken a designer, a maker, a mind—intelligence? And do you have any reason to believe that intelligence can exist apart from personality?

Superb organization requires a superb organizer

[16] We cannot get around it: Superb organization requires a superb organizer. Nothing in our experience indicates that anything organized happens by chance, by accident. Rather, our entire experience in life shows that everything organized must have an organizer. Every machine, computer, building, yes, even pencil and paper, had a maker, an organizer. Logically, the far more complex and awesome organization in the universe must have had an organizer too.

Law Requires a Lawmaker

[17] Also, the entire universe, from atoms to galaxies, is governed by definite physical laws. There are laws for governing heat, light, sound and gravity, for example. As physicist Stephen W. Hawking said: "The more we examine the universe, we find it is not arbitrary at all but obeys certain well-defined laws that operate in different areas. It

The universe "obeys certain well-defined laws"

---

15. What does the precise design and organization of the universe indicate?
16. To what conclusion must we come regarding the universe?
17. How is law involved in the universe?

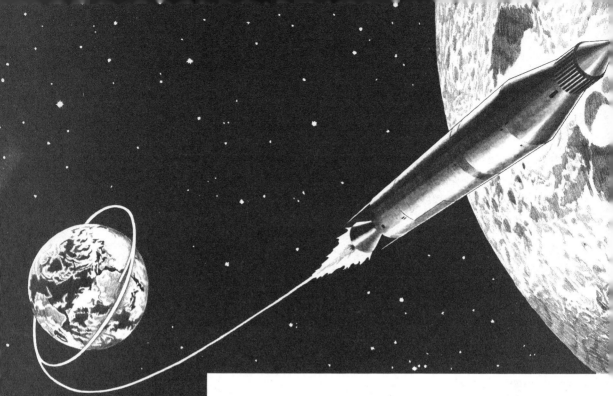

The flight of a rocket into orbit requires adherence to laws of motion and gravity. Such laws require a lawmaker

seems very reasonable to suppose that there may be some unifying principles, so that all laws are part of some bigger law."[7]

[18] Rocket expert Wernher von Braun went a step further when he stated: "The natural laws of the universe are so precise that we have no difficulty building a spaceship to fly to the moon and can time the flight with the precision of a fraction of a second. These laws must have been set by somebody."[8] Scientists who want a rocket to orbit the earth, or the moon, must work in harmony with such universal laws if they are to be successful.

[19] When we think of laws, we acknowledge that they came from a lawmaking entity. A traffic sign that says "Stop" certainly has behind it some person or group of persons who originated the law. What, then, about the comprehensive laws that govern the material universe? Such brilliantly conceived laws surely bear witness to a supremely intelligent lawmaker.

18. What did a rocket expert conclude?
19. What does the existence of laws require?

124

The Organizer and Lawmaker

[20] After commenting on all the special conditions of order and law that are so apparent in the universe, *Science News* observed: "Contemplation of these things disturbs cosmologists because it seems as if such particular and precise conditions could hardly have arisen at random. One way to deal with the question is to say the whole thing was contrived and lay it on Divine Providence."[9]

Traffic laws had to originate in minds

[21] Many persons, including many scientists, are not willing to concede that. But others are willing to acknowledge what the evidence keeps insisting —intelligence. They acknowledge that such colossal size, precision and law as exist throughout the universe could never have happened just by accident. All these things must be the products of a superior mind.

[22] This is the conclusion expressed by one Bible writer who said regarding the physical heavens: "Raise your eyes high up and see. Who has created these things? It is the One who is bringing forth the army of them even by number, all of whom he calls even by name." That "One" is identified as "the Creator of the heavens and the Grand One stretching them out."—Isaiah 40:26; 42:5.

Source of Energy

[23] Universal laws govern existing matter. But where did all the matter come from? In *Cosmos,* Carl Sagan says: "At the beginning of this universe, there were no galaxies, stars or planets, no life or civilizations." He refers to the change from that state to the present universe as "the most awesome transformation of matter and energy that we have been privileged to glimpse."[10]

"It seems as if such particular and precise conditions could hardly have arisen at random"

---

20. What observation was made by *Science News?*
21. What are some persons willing to conclude?
22. How did one Bible writer identify the Originator of the universe?
23, 24. How can matter be produced?

125

The atomic bomb demonstrated that matter and energy are related

²⁴ That is the key to understanding how the universe could have come into existence: It must have involved a transformation of energy and matter. This relationship was verified by Einstein's famous formula, $E=mc^2$ (energy equals mass times the speed of light squared). One conclusion that derives from this formula is that matter can be produced from energy, just as tremendous energy can be produced from matter. The atomic bomb proved the latter. Thus, astrophysicist Josip Kleczek stated: "Most and possibly all elementary particles may be created by materialization of energy."[11]

²⁵ Hence, there is scientific evidence that a source of limitless energy would have the raw material to create the substance of the universe. The Bible writer quoted earlier noted that this source of energy is a living, intelligent personality, saying: "Due to the *abundance of dynamic energy,* he also being *vigorous in power,* not one of them [the heavenly bodies] is missing." Thus, from the Biblical standpoint, this source of boundless energy was behind what Genesis 1:1 describes: "In the beginning God created the heavens and the earth."

Beginning Not Chaotic

Do bomb explosions cause buildings to become better organized?

²⁶ Today, scientists generally acknowledge that the universe did have a beginning. One prominent theory that attempts to describe this beginning is known as the Big Bang. "Almost all recent discussions of the origin of the universe are based on the Big Bang theory," notes Francis Crick.[12] Jastrow refers to this cosmic "explosion" as "literally the moment of creation."[13] But, as astrophysicist John Gribbin admitted in *New Scientist,* though scientists "claim, by and large, to be able to describe in great detail" what happened after this "moment," what brought about "the instant of creation re-

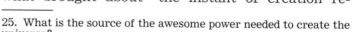

25. What is the source of the awesome power needed to create the universe?
26. What do scientists generally acknowledge today?

mains a mystery." And, he mused, "maybe God did make it, after all."[14]

27 However, most scientists are not willing to attribute this "instant" to God. Hence, the explosion usually is said to have been chaotic, like the explosion of a nuclear bomb. But does this type of explosion result in better organization? Do the bombs that fall on cities in wartime produce superbly designed buildings, streets and signs with traffic laws? On the contrary, such explosions cause wreckage, disorder, chaos, disintegration. And when the explosive device is nuclear the disorganization is total, as experienced by the Japanese cities of Hiroshima and Nagasaki in 1945.

28 No, a mere "explosion" could not create our awesome universe with its amazing order, design and law. Only a mighty organizer and lawmaker could direct the powerful forces at work so that they would result in superb organization and law. Hence, scientific evidence and reason provide solid backing for the Bible's declaration: "The heavens are declaring the glory of God; and of the work of his hands the expanse is telling."—Psalm 19:1.

29 Thus, the Bible comes to grips with questions that evolutionary theory has not clearly addressed. Instead of leaving us in the dark as to what is behind the origin of all things, the Bible tells us the answer simply and understandably. It confirms the observations of science, as well as our own, that nothing comes into existence by itself. Although we personally were not on hand when the universe was constructed, it is evident that it had to have a Master Builder, as the Bible reasons: "Every house is constructed by someone, but he that constructed all things is God."—Hebrews 3:4.

"Every house is constructed by someone, but he that constructed all things is God."—Hebrews 3:4

27. Why is the Big Bang theory too limited?
28. What must be concluded about the powerful forces that worked to create the universe?
29. What is confirmed by the observations of science as well as our own?

127

Chapter 10

Evidence
From a Unique Planet

OUR planet Earth is truly a wonder—a rare, beautiful jewel in space. Astronauts have reported that, viewed from space, the earth's blue skies and white clouds "made it by far the most inviting object they could see."[1]

[2] However, it is much more than just beautiful. "The greatest of all cosmological scientific puzzles, confounding all our efforts to comprehend it, is the earth," wrote Lewis Thomas in *Discover*. He added: "We are only now beginning to appreciate how strange and splendid it is, how it catches the breath, the loveliest object afloat around the sun, enclosed in its own blue bubble of atmosphere, manufacturing and breathing its own oxygen, fixing its own nitrogen from the air into its own soil, generating its own weather."[2]

[3] Also of interest is this fact: Of all the planets in our solar system, only on Earth have scientists found life. And what marvelous, abundant varieties of living things there are—microscopic organisms, insects, plants, fish, birds, animals and humans. In addition, the earth is a vast storehouse of wealth that contains everything needed to sustain all that life. Truly, as the book *The Earth* expressed it, "The earth is the wonder of the universe, a unique sphere."[3]

"The earth is the wonder of the universe, a unique sphere"

1, 2. What do observers say about our planet Earth?
3. What does the book *The Earth* say about our planet, and why?

129

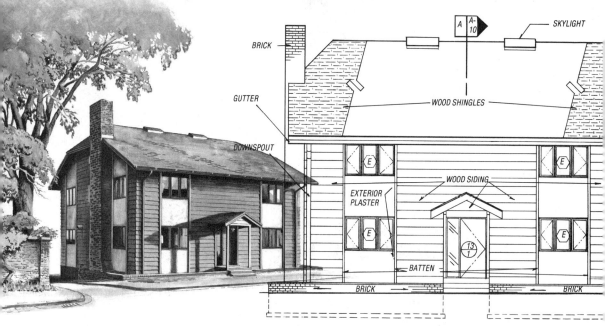

BRICK

GUTTER

DOWNSPOUT

A | A-10

SKYLIGHT

WOOD SHINGLES

E | E

E | E

EXTERIOR PLASTER

WOOD SIDING

13

E | E

BATTEN

BRICK | BRICK

Since every house must have a designer and builder, what of our far more intricate and better-equipped earth?

[4] To illustrate how unique the earth is, imagine that you are in a barren desert, devoid of all life. Suddenly you come upon a beautiful house. The house has air conditioning, heating, plumbing and electricity. Its refrigerator and cupboards are filled with food. Its basement contains fuel and other supplies. Now, suppose you asked someone where all of this came from, in such a barren desert. What would you think if that person answered, "It just happened to appear there by chance"? Would you believe that? Or would you take for granted that it had a designer and builder?

[5] All the other planets that scientists have probed are devoid of life. But Earth teems with life, sustained by very complex systems that provide light, air, heat, water and food, all in exquisite balance. It shows evidence of having been specially built to accommodate living things comfortably—like a magnificent house. And logically, as one of the Bible's penmen argues: "Every house is constructed by someone, but he that constructed all things is God." Yes, the infinitely greater and more amazing "house"—our planet Earth—requires the exis-

4. What illustration can be used to show how unique the earth is, and what conclusion must we draw?
5. What Biblical illustration is appropriate to our planet Earth?

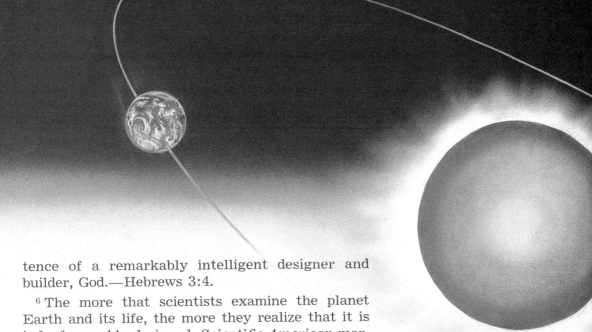

tence of a remarkably intelligent designer and builder, God.—Hebrews 3:4.

6 The more that scientists examine the planet Earth and its life, the more they realize that it is indeed superbly designed. *Scientific American* marvels: "As we look out into the universe and identify the many accidents of physics and astronomy that have worked together to our benefit, it almost seems as if the universe must in some sense have known that we were coming."[4] And *Science News* admitted: "It seems as if such particular and precise conditions could hardly have arisen at random."[5]

The earth's orbital speed keeps it at just the right distance from the sun

Right Distance From the Sun

7 Among the many precise conditions vital to life on the earth is the amount of light and heat received from the sun. The earth gets only a small fraction of the sun's energy. Yet, it is just the right amount required to sustain life. This is because the earth is just the right distance from the sun—an average 93,000,000 miles. If the earth were much closer to the sun or farther away from it, temperatures would be too hot or too cold for life.

---

6. How have some acknowledged that the planet Earth does give evidence of intelligent design?
7. How does the earth receive just the right amount of energy in the form of light and heat from the sun?

Summer

Autumn

The earth's tilt allows for delightful seasonal changes

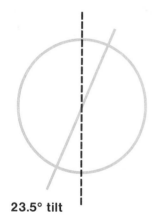

23.5° tilt

[8] As it orbits the sun once a year the earth travels at a speed of about 66,600 miles an hour. That speed is just right to offset the gravitational pull of the sun and keep the earth at the proper distance. If that speed were decreased, the earth would be pulled toward the sun. In time, Earth could become a scorched wasteland like Mercury, the planet closest to the sun. Mercury's daytime temperature is over 600 degrees Fahrenheit. However, if Earth's orbital speed were increased, it would move farther away from the sun and could become an icy waste like Pluto, the planet whose orbit reaches farthest from the sun. Pluto's temperature is about 300 degrees below zero Fahrenheit.

[9] In addition, the earth consistently makes a complete rotation on its axis every 24 hours. This provides regular periods of light and darkness. But what if the earth rotated on its axis, say, only once a year? It would mean that the same side of the earth would be facing the sun all year long. That

8. Why is the earth's orbital speed around the sun so vital?
9. Why is it important that the earth rotate on its axis with a certain frequency?

Winter   **Spring**

side would likely become a furnacelike desert, while the side away from the sun would likely become a sub-zero wasteland. Few, if any, living things could exist in those extreme circumstances.

[10] As Earth rotates on its axis, it is tilted 23.5 degrees in relation to the sun. If the earth were not tilted, there would be no change of seasons. Climate would be the same all the time. While this would not make life impossible, it would make it less interesting and would drastically change the present crop cycles in many places. If the earth were tilted much more, there would be extremely hot summers and extremely cold winters. But the tilt of 23.5 degrees allows for the delightful changing of seasons with their interesting variety. In many parts of the earth there are refreshing springtimes with plants and trees awakening and beautiful flowers coming into bloom, warm summers that allow for all kinds of outdoor activity, crisp autumn weather with gorgeous displays of leaves changing colors, and winters with beautiful scenes of snow-draped mountains, forests and fields.

10. How does the earth's tilt affect climate and crops?

133

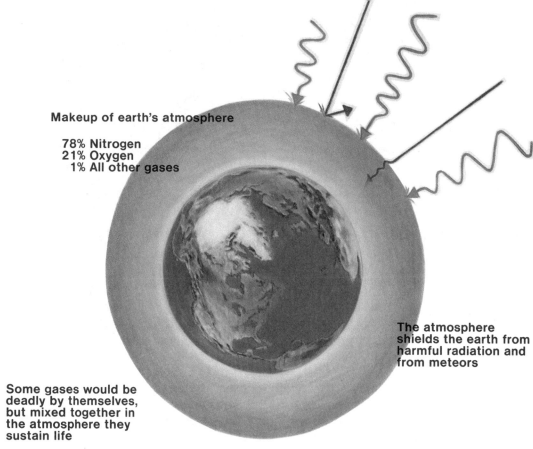

Makeup of earth's atmosphere

**78% Nitrogen
21% Oxygen
1% All other gases**

**The atmosphere
shields the earth from
harmful radiation and
from meteors**

**Some gases would be
deadly by themselves,
but mixed together in
the atmosphere they
sustain life**

Our Amazing Atmosphere

[11] Also unique—indeed, amazing—is the atmosphere that surrounds our earth. No other planet in our solar system has it. Nor does our moon. That is why astronauts needed space suits to survive there. But no space suits are needed on the earth, because our atmosphere contains the right proportions of gases that are absolutely essential for life. Some of those gases, by themselves, are deadly. But because air contains safe proportions of these gases, we can breathe them without harm.

[12] One of those gases is oxygen, making up 21 percent of the air we breathe. Without it, humans and animals would die within minutes. But too much oxygen would endanger our existence. Why? Pure oxygen becomes toxic if breathed too long. In

11. What makes the earth's atmosphere so unique?
12. (a) How is it evident that we have just the right amount of oxygen? (b) What vital function does nitrogen have?

addition, the more oxygen there is, the more easily things burn. If there were too much oxygen in the atmosphere, combustible materials would become highly flammable. Fires would easily burst forth and would be difficult to control. Wisely, oxygen is diluted with other gases, especially nitrogen, which makes up 78 percent of the atmosphere. But nitrogen is much more than just a dilutant. During thunderstorms, millions of lightning bolts occur earth wide every day. This lightning causes some nitrogen to combine with oxygen. The compounds produced are carried to the earth by rain, and plants make use of them as fertilizer.

[13] Carbon dioxide makes up less than one percent of the atmosphere. What good is such a small amount? Without it, plant life would die. That small amount is what plants need to take in, giving off oxygen in return. Humans and animals breathe in the oxygen and exhale carbon dioxide. An increasing percentage of carbon dioxide in the atmosphere would tend to be harmful to humans and animals. A decreasing percentage could not support plant life. What a marvelous, precise, self-sustaining cycle has been arranged for plant, animal and human life!

Without oxygen, humans and animals would die within minutes

[14] The atmosphere does more than sustain life. It serves as a protective shell too. About 15 miles above the ground, a thin layer of ozone gas filters out harmful radiation from the sun. Without this ozone layer, such radiation could destroy life on earth. Also, the atmosphere shields the earth from bombardment by meteors. Most meteors never reach the ground because they burn up in their descent through the atmosphere, appearing to us as falling stars. Otherwise, millions of meteors would strike all parts of the earth, resulting in extensive damage to life and property.

13. What part does the right amount of carbon dioxide play in the life cycle?
14, 15. How does the atmosphere serve as a protective shell?

A night sky can have a beauty all its own

[15] In addition to being a protective shell, the atmosphere keeps the warmth of the earth from being lost to the coldness of space. And the atmosphere is itself kept from escaping by the earth's gravitational pull. That gravity is just strong enough to accomplish this, but not so strong that our freedom of movement is hampered.

[16] Not only is the atmosphere vital for life, but one of the more beautiful sights is the changing sky. Its scope and grandeur simply stagger the imagination. The earth is enveloped with the sky's endlessly majestic and colorful panoramas. In the east a golden glow announces the dawn, while the western sky bids the day farewell in glorious displays of pink, orange, red and purple. White billowy, cottonlike clouds proclaim a fine spring or summer day; an autumn mantle of clouds like lamb's wool says that winter is approaching. At night the sky is magnificent in its starry splendor, and a moonlit night has a beauty all its own.

[17] What an amazing provision our earth's atmo-

16. What can be said about the beauty of the sky?
17. How did a writer comment on the sky, and to whom does the credit belong?

sphere is, in every way! As a writer in *The New England Journal of Medicine* commented: "Taken all in all, the sky is a miraculous achievement. It works, and for what it is designed to accomplish it is as infallible as anything in nature. I doubt whether any of us could think of a way to improve on it, beyond maybe shifting a local cloud from here to there on occasion."[6] This comment calls to mind what a man millenniums ago recognized when confronted with such remarkable things—that they are "the wonderful works of the One perfect in knowledge." He meant, of course, "the Creator of the heavens and the Grand One stretching them out."—Job 37:16; Isaiah 42:5.

"The sky is a miraculous achievement"

Water—An Extraordinary Substance

[18] The earth contains vast supplies of water with properties essential for life. It is more abundant than any other substance. Among its many advantageous qualities is that it occurs as a gas (water vapor), a liquid (water), and a solid (ice)—all within earth's temperature range. Too, the thousands of raw materials that humans, animals and plants need must be transported in a fluid, such as blood or sap. Water is most ideal for this because it will dissolve more substances than any other liquid. Without water, nutrition could not continue, since living organisms depend on water to dissolve the substances on which they feed.

Without water, animals and plants could not get the nutrients they need

[19] Water is also extraordinary in the way it freezes. As water in lakes and seas cools, it becomes heavier and sinks. This forces the lighter, warmer water to rise to the top. Yet, as water approaches the freezing point, the process reverses! The colder water now becomes lighter and rises. When it freezes into ice, it floats. The ice acts as an insulator and keeps the deeper waters underneath from freezing,

---

18. What are some qualities of water that make it extraordinary?
19. What unusual quality does freezing water have, and why is that so important?

Water sinks as it cools, but rises just before freezing. This prevents the earth from becoming a frozen planet

thus protecting marine life. Without this unique quality, every winter more and more ice would sink to the bottom where the sun's rays could not melt it the following summer. Soon, much of the water in rivers, lakes and even the oceans would become solid ice. The earth would turn into an icy planet that would be inhospitable to life.

[20] Extraordinary, too, is the way that regions far from rivers, lakes and seas get life-sustaining water. Every second, the sun's heat changes thousands of millions of gallons of water into vapor. This vapor, lighter than air, floats upward and forms clouds in the sky. Wind and air currents move these clouds, and, under the right conditions, the moisture drops as rain. But raindrops tend to grow only to a certain size. What if this were not so, and raindrops became gigantic in size? That would be disastrous! Instead, rain usually comes down in the right size, and gently, seldom hurting even a blade of grass or the most delicate flower. What masterful, considerate design is evident in water!—Psalm 104:1, 10-14; Ecclesiastes 1:7.

"The Productive Land"

[21] One of the Biblical penmen describes God as "the One firmly establishing the productive land by his wisdom." (Jeremiah 10:12) And this "productive land"—the soil of planet Earth—is impressive. Wis-

20. How is rain formed, and why does the size of raindrops show thoughtful design?
21, 22. What wisdom is shown in the makeup of "the productive land"?

138

Light from the sun, carbon dioxide from the air, and water and chemicals from the soil combine miraculously to produce food

dom is evident in its makeup. Soil has qualities essential for plant growth. Plants combine the nutrients and water in the soil with carbon dioxide from the air, in the presence of light, to produce food.—Compare Ezekiel 34:26, 27.

22 The soil contains chemical elements that are needed to sustain human and animal life. But vegetation must first convert those elements into forms that can be assimilated by the body. Cooperating in this are tiny living organisms. And many millions of them can be found in just a spoonful of soil! They are of countless different designs, each working to convert dead leaves, grass and other waste matter back to usable form, or to loosen up the soil so that air and water can get in. Certain bacteria convert nitrogen into compounds that plants need for growth. Topsoil is improved as burrowing worms and insects continually bring up particles of subsoil to the surface.

23 True, because of misuse and other factors some soil is damaged. But this damage need not be permanent. The earth has amazing built-in powers of restoration. This can be noted in places where fires or volcanic eruptions have devastated the land. In time, these areas once again flourish with vegetation. And when pollution is controlled, land is re-

23. What powers of restoration does the soil have?

The earth has amazing powers of recovery. In a short time new growth emerges

stored, even land that was turned into a barren waste. Most important of all, to deal with the basic problem behind misuse of the soil, earth's Creator has purposed to "bring to ruin those ruining the earth" and to preserve it as the eternal home he originally prepared for mankind.—Revelation 11:18; Isaiah 45:18.

Not Just Chance

24 In thinking over the foregoing, here are some things to consider: Was it undirected chance that placed the earth at just the right distance from the

---

24. What questions can we ask about undirected chance?

sun, its source of energy in the form of light and heat? Was it mere chance that caused the earth to move around the sun at just the right speed, to rotate on its axis every 24 hours, and to have just the correct angle of tilt? Was it chance that provided the earth with a protective, life-sustaining atmosphere having just the right mixture of gases? Was it chance that gave the earth the water and soil needed to grow food? Was it chance that provided so many delicious and colorful fruits, vegetables and other foods? Was it chance that caused so much beauty to exist in the sky, the mountains, the streams and lakes, the flowers, plants and trees, and in so many other delightful living things?

Was it undirected chance that provided so many delightful things for our enjoyment?

25 Many have concluded that all of this could hardly be due to undirected chance. Instead, they see the unmistakable stamp of thoughtful, intelligent, deliberate design everywhere. Recognizing that, they feel it is only right that the beneficiaries "fear God and give him glory" because he is "the One who made the heaven and the earth and sea and fountains of waters."—Revelation 14:7.

The earth bears the unmistakable stamp of deliberate design

---

25. What conclusion about our unique planet have many people drawn?

Chapter 11

The Amazing Design of Living Things

Designer needed

No designer needed?

WHEN anthropologists dig in the earth and find a triangular piece of sharp flint, they conclude that it must have been designed by someone to be the tip of an arrow. Such things designed for a purpose, scientists agree, could not be products of chance.

[2] When it comes to living things, however, the same logic is often abandoned. A designer is not considered necessary. But the simplest single-celled organism, or just the DNA of its genetic code, is far more complex than a shaped piece of flint. Yet evolutionists insist that these had no designer but were shaped by a series of chance events.

[3] However, Darwin recognized the need for some designing force and gave natural selection the job. "Natural selection," he said, "is daily and hourly scrutinising, throughout the world, the slightest variations; rejecting those that are bad, preserving and adding up all that are good."[1] That view, however, is now losing favor.

[4] Stephen Gould reports that many contemporary evolutionists now say that substantial change "may not be subject to natural selection and may spread through populations at random."[2] Gordon Taylor

1, 2. (a) What shows that scientists recognize the need for a designer? (b) Yet how do they then reverse themselves?
3. What need did Darwin recognize, and how did he attempt to fill it?
4. How are views on natural selection changing?

agrees: "Natural selection explains a small part of what occurs: the bulk remains unexplained."[3] Geologist David Raup says: "A currently important alternative to natural selection has to do with the effects of pure chance."[4] But is "pure chance" a designer? Is it capable of producing the complexities that are the fabric of life?

[5] Zoologist Richard Lewontin said that organisms "appear to have been carefully and artfully designed." He views them as "the chief evidence of a Supreme Designer."[5] It will be useful to consider some of this evidence.

Little Things

[6] Let us start with the smallest of living things: single-celled organisms. A biologist said that single-celled animals can "catch food, digest it, get rid of wastes, move around, build houses, engage in sexual activity" and "with no tissues, no organs, no hearts and no minds—really have everything we've got."[6]

[7] Diatoms, one-celled organisms, take silicon and oxygen from seawater and make glass, with which they construct tiny "pillboxes" to contain their green chlorophyll. They are extolled by one scientist for both their importance and their beauty: "These green leaves enclosed in jewel boxes are pastures for nine tenths of the food of everything that lives in the seas." A large part of their food value is in the oil that diatoms make, which also helps them bob buoyantly near the surface where their chlorophyll can bask in sunlight.

[8] Their beautiful glass-box coverings, this same scientist tells us, come in a "bewildering variety of shapes—circles, squares, shields, triangles, ovals,

Diatoms

Designs in glass skeletons of microscopic plants

5. What recognition does a zoologist give to design and to its originator?
6. Are single-celled organisms really simple?
7. How and for what purpose do diatoms make glass, and how important are they to life in the seas?
8. With what complex shapes do diatoms cover themselves?

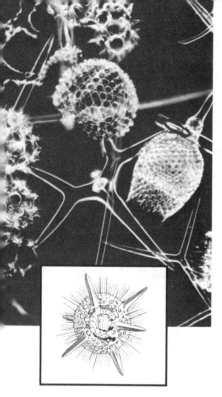

rectangles—always exquisitely ornamented with geometric etchings. These are filigreed in pure glass with such fine skill that a human hair would have to be sliced lengthwise into four hundred slices to fit between the marks."[7]

[9] One group of ocean-dwelling animals, called radiolarians, make glass and with it build "glass sunbursts, with long thin transparent spikelets radiating from a central crystal sphere." Or "glass struts are built into hexagons and used to make simple geodesic domes." Of a certain microscopic builder it is said: "One geodesic dome will not do for this superarchitect; it has to be three lacelike fretted glass domes, one inside another."[8] Words fail to describe these marvels of design—it takes pictures to do so.

Radiolarians: designs in glass skeletons of microscopic animals

[10] Sponges are made up of millions of cells, but only a few different kinds. A college textbook explains: "The cells are not organized into tissues or organs, yet there is a form of recognition among the cells that holds them together and organizes them."[9] If a sponge is mashed through a cloth and separated into its millions of cells, those cells will come together and rebuild the sponge. Sponges construct skeletons of glass that are very beautiful. One of the most amazing is Venus's-flower-basket.

Venus's-flower-basket

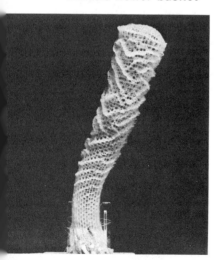

[11] Of it, one scientist says: "When you look at a complex sponge skeleton such as that made of silica spicules which is known as [Venus's-flower-basket], the imagination is baffled. How could quasi-independent microscopic cells collaborate to secrete a million glassy splinters and construct such an intricate and beautiful lattice? We do not know."[10] But one thing we do know: Chance is not the likely designer.

9. How complex are some of the houses radiolarians build?
10, 11. (a) What are sponges, and what happens to the individual cells when a sponge is completely broken up? (b) What question about sponge skeletons do evolutionists find unanswerable, but what do we know?

Partnerships

[12] Many cases exist where two organisms appear *designed* to live together. Such partnerships are examples of symbiosis (living together). Certain figs and wasps need each other in order to reproduce. Termites eat wood but need the protozoa in their bodies to digest it. Similarly, cattle, goats and camels could not digest the cellulose in grass without the help of bacteria and protozoa living inside them. A report says: "The part of a cow's stomach where that digestion takes place has a volume of about 100 quarts—and contains 10 billion microorganisms in each drop."[11] Algae and fungi team up and become lichens. Only then can they grow on bare rock to start turning rock into soil.

[13] Stinging ants live in the hollow thorns of acacia trees. They keep leaf-eating insects off the tree and they cut up and kill vines that try to climb on the tree. In return, the tree secretes a sugary fluid that the ants relish, and it also produces small false fruit, which serves as food for the ants. Did the ant first protect the tree and then the tree rewarded it with fruit? Or did the tree make fruit for the ant and the ant then thanked it with protection? Or did it all chance to happen at once?

[14] Many cases of such cooperation exist between insects and flowers. Insects pollinate flowers, and in return flowers feed insects pollen and nectar. Some flowers produce two kinds of pollen. One fertilizes seeds, the other is sterile but feeds insect visitors. Many flowers have special markings and smells to guide insects to the nectar. En route the insects pollinate the flower. Some flowers have trigger mechanisms. When insects touch the trigger they get swatted by the pollen-containing anthers.

Many flowers have signposts to guide insects to hidden nectar

---

12. What is symbiosis, and what are some examples?
13. The partnership between stinging ants and acacia trees raises what questions?
14. What special provisions and mechanisms do flowers use to attract insects for pollination?

145

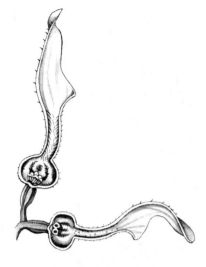

Some flowers have waxed slides to trap insects so that pollination can be accomplished

[15] For example, the Dutchman's-pipe cannot pollinate itself but needs insects to bring in pollen from another flower. The plant has a tubular leaf that envelops its flower, and this leaf is coated with wax. Insects, attracted by the smell of the flower, land on the leaf and plunge down the slippery slide to a chamber at the bottom. There, ripe stigmas receive the pollen that the insects brought in, and pollination takes place. But for three more days the insects are trapped there by hairs and the waxed sides. After that, the flower's own pollen ripens and dusts the insects. Only then do the hairs wilt, and the waxed slide bends over until it is level. The insects walk out and, with their new supply of pollen, fly to another Dutchman's-pipe to pollinate it. The insects do not mind their three-day visit, since they feast on nectar stored there for them. Did all of this happen by chance? Or did it happen by intelligent design?

[16] Some types of *Ophrys* orchids have on their petals a picture of a female wasp, complete with eyes, antennae and wings. It even gives off the odor of a female in mating condition! The male comes to mate, but only pollinates the flower. Another orchid, the bucket orchid, has a fermented nectar that makes the bee wobbly on its feet; it slips into a bucket of liquid and the only way out is to wriggle under a rod that dusts the bee with pollen.

Nature's "Factories"

[17] Green leaves of plants feed the world, directly or indirectly. But they cannot function without the help of tiny roots. Millions of rootlets—each root tip fitted with a protective cap, each cap lubricated with oil—push their way through the soil. Root hairs behind the oily cap absorb water and miner-

Why does this orchid have the likeness of a female wasp?

15. How does the Dutchman's-pipe ensure cross-pollination, and what questions does this raise?
16. How do some *Ophrys* orchids and the bucket orchid get themselves pollinated?
17. How do leaves and roots work together in nourishing plants?

146

als, which travel up minute channels in the sapwood to the leaves. In the leaves sugars and amino acids are made, and these nutrients are sent throughout the tree and into the roots.

[18] Certain features of the circulatory system of trees and plants are so amazing that many scientists regard them as almost miraculous. First, how is the water pumped two or three hundred feet above the ground? Root pressure starts it on its way, but in the trunk another mechanism takes over. Water molecules hold together by cohesion. Because of this cohesion, as water evaporates from the leaves the tiny columns of water are pulled up like ropes—ropes reaching from the roots to the leaves, and traveling at up to 200 feet an hour. This system, it is said, could lift water in a tree about two miles high! As excess water evaporates from the leaves (called transpiration), billions of tons of water are recycled into the air, once again to fall as rain—a perfectly designed system!

[19] There is more. The leaves need nitrates or nitrites from the ground to make vital amino acids. Some amounts are put into the soil by lightning and by certain free-living bacteria. Nitrogen compounds in adequate quantities are also formed by legumes —plants such as peas, clover, beans and alfalfa. Certain bacteria enter their roots, the roots provide the bacteria with carbohydrates, and the bacteria change, or fix, nitrogen from the soil into usable nitrates and nitrites, producing some 200 pounds per acre each year.

[20] There is still more. Green leaves take energy from the sun, carbon dioxide from the air and water

---

18. (a) How does water get from roots to leaves, and what shows that this system is more than adequate? (b) What is transpiration, and how does it contribute to the water cycle?
19. What vital service is performed by the partnership of some roots and certain bacteria?
20. (a) What does photosynthesis do, where does it happen, and who understands the process? (b) How does one biologist view it? (c) What may green plants be called, how do they excel, and what questions are appropriate?

The cohesion between water molecules, it is said, could lift water in a tree two miles high!

The Amazing Designs of Seeds

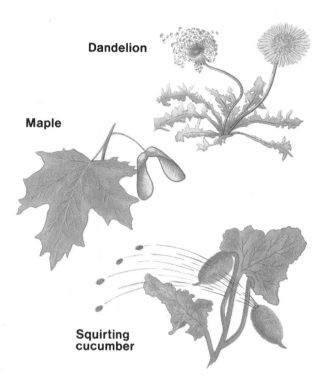

Dandelion

Maple

Squirting cucumber

Seeds Ripe and Ready to Go!

A variety of ingenious designs send seeds on their way! Orchid seeds are so light that they float off like dust. Dandelion seeds come equipped with parachutes. Maple seeds have wings and flutter off like butterflies. Some water plants equip their seeds with air-filled floats and off they sail.

Some plants have pods that snap open and the seeds are catapulted out. The slippery seeds of witch hazel are first squeezed, then shot out from the fruit, like watermelon seeds that children squirt from thumb and forefinger. The squirting cucumber uses hydraulics. As it grows the skin thickens inwardly, the fluid center comes under increasing pressure, and by the time the seeds are ripe the pressure is so great that it blows the stem out like a cork from a bottle, and the seeds shoot out.

Seeds That Measure Rainfall

Some desert annuals have seeds that refuse to sprout until a half inch or more of rain has fallen. They also seem to know which direction the water comes from—if it rains down from above they will sprout, but if it is being soaked up from below, they will not. In the soil there are salts that prevent the seeds from sprouting. It takes rain from above to leach out these salts. Water that is soaked up from below cannot do this.

If these desert annuals started growing after only a light shower, they would die. It takes a heavy rain to put enough moisture into the soil to save the plants from later dry spells. So they wait for it. Chance—or design?

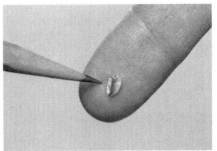

A Giant in a Tiny Package

One of the smallest seeds has packaged within it the biggest living thing on earth—the giant sequoia tree. It grows over 300 feet high. Four feet above the ground its diameter may be 36 feet. One tree may contain enough wood to build 50 six-room houses. The two-foot-thick bark is flavored with tannin that repels insects, and its spongy, fibrous texture makes it almost as fireproof as asbestos. Its roots cover three or four acres. It lives over 3,000 years.

Yet the seeds that a sequoia tree rains down by the millions are not much bigger than a pinhead surrounded by tiny wings. A puny man standing at a sequoia's base can only gaze upward in silent awe at its massive grandeur. Does it make sense to believe that the shaping of this majestic giant and of the tiny seed that packages it was not by design?

149

Musical Virtuosos

The mockingbird is famous as a mimic. One imitated 55 other birds in an hour. But it is the mockingbird's original compositions of melodious outpourings that keep listeners spellbound. Surely they go far beyond the few simple notes needed to declare territorial claims. Is it for their pleasure —and ours?

The musician wrens of South America are no less amazing. Mated pairs sing duets, as do other tropical bird pairs. Their performances are unique, as one reference book notes: "The female and male sing either the same songs *together*, different songs, or different parts of the same song *alternately*; they may be so exactly timed that the total song sounds as though uttered by one bird."[a] How beautiful are these soft musical dialogues as the mated wrens communicate with each other! A mere accidental occurrence?

from the plant's roots to make sugar and give off oxygen. The process is called photosynthesis, and it happens in cell bodies called chloroplasts—so small that 400,000 can fit into the period at the end of this sentence. Scientists do not understand the process fully. "There are about seventy separate chemical reactions involved in photosynthesis," one biol-

150

ogist said. "It is truly a miraculous event."[12] Green plants have been called nature's "factories"—beautiful, quiet, nonpolluting, producing oxygen, recycling water and feeding the world. Did they just happen by chance? Is that truly believable?

[21] Some of the world's most famous scientists have found it hard to believe. They see intelligence in the natural world. Nobel-prize-winning physicist Robert A. Millikan, although a believer in evolution, did say at a meeting of the American Physical Society: "There's a Divinity that shapes our ends . . . A purely materialistic philosophy is to me the height of unintelligence. Wise men in all the ages have always seen enough to at least make them reverent." In his speech he quoted Albert Einstein's notable words, wherein Einstein said that he did "try humbly to comprehend even an infinitesimal part of the intelligence manifest in nature."[13]

"Seventy separate chemical reactions [are] involved in photosynthesis. It is truly a miraculous event"

[22] Evidence of design surrounds us, in endless variety and amazing intricacy, indicating a superior intelligence. This conclusion is also voiced in the Bible, where design is attributed to a Creator whose "invisible qualities are clearly seen from the world's creation onward, because they are perceived by the things made, even his eternal power and Godship, so that they are inexcusable."—Romans 1:20.

[23] With so much evidence of design in the life around us, it does seem "inexcusable" to say that undirected chance is behind it. Hence, for the psalmist to credit an intelligent Creator is certainly not unreasonable: "How many your works are, O Jehovah! All of them in wisdom you have made. The earth is full of your productions. As for this sea so great and wide, there there are moving things without number, living creatures, small as well as great."—Psalm 104:24, 25.

21, 22. (a) What did two famous scientists say in testifying to the intelligence in the natural world? (b) How does the Bible reason on this matter?
23. What reasonable conclusion does the psalmist express?

Chapter 12

Who Did It First?

"I HAVE the suspicion," one biologist said, "that we're not the innovators we think we are; we're merely the repeaters."[1] Many times, human inventors only repeat what plants and animals have been doing for thousands of years. This copying from living things is so prevalent that it has been given its own name—*bionics*.

[2] Another scientist says that practically all the fundamental areas of human technology "have been opened up and utilized to advantage by living things . . . before the human mind learned to understand and master their functions." Interestingly, he adds:

1. What did a biologist say about human inventors?
2. What comparison did another scientist make between human technology and that of nature?

"In many areas, human technology is still lagging far behind nature."[2]

[3] As you reflect on these complex abilities of living creatures that human inventors have attempted to copy, does it seem reasonable to believe that they happened by chance alone? And happened, not just once, but many times in unrelated creatures? Are these not the kind of intricate designs that experience teaches can only be the product of a brilliant designer? Do you really think that chance alone could create what it later took gifted men to copy? Bear in mind such questions as you consider the following examples:

[4] AIR CONDITIONING. Modern technology cools many homes. But long before, termites also cooled theirs, and they still do. Their nest is in the center of a large mound. From it, warm air rises into a network of air ducts near the surface. There stale air diffuses out the porous sides, and fresh cool air seeps in and descends into an air chamber at the bottom of the mound. From there it circulates into the nest. Some mounds have openings at the bottom where fresh air comes in, and in hot weather, water brought up from underground evaporates, thus cooling the air. How do millions of blind workers coordinate their efforts to build such ingeniously designed structures? Biologist Lewis Thomas answers: "The plain fact that they exhibit something like a collective intelligence is a mystery."[3]

[5] AIRPLANES. The design of airplane wings has benefited over the years from the study of the wings of birds. The curvature of the bird's wing gives the lift needed to overcome the downward pull of gravity. But when the wing is tilted up too much, there is the danger of stalling. To avoid a

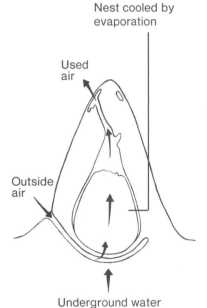

Nest cooled by evaporation

Used air

Outside air

Underground water

---

3. What questions should be kept in mind as examples of bionics are considered?
4. (a) How do termites cool their homes? (b) What question are scientists unable to answer?
5-8. What have airplane designers learned from wings of birds?

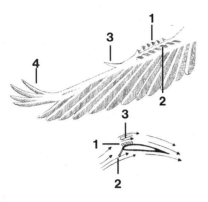

stall, the bird has on the leading edges of its wings rows, or flaps, of feathers that pop up as wing tilt increases (1, 2). These flaps maintain lift by keeping the main airstream from separating from the wing surface.

[6] Still another feature for controlling turbulence and preventing "stalling out" is the alula (3), a small bunch of feathers that the bird can raise up like a thumb.

[7] At the tips of the wings of both birds and airplanes, eddies form and they produce drag. Birds minimize this in two ways. Some, like swifts and albatross, have long, slender wings with small tips, and this design eliminates most of the eddies. Others, like big hawks and vultures, have broad wings that would make big eddies, but this is avoided when the birds spread out, like fingers, the pinions at the ends of their wings. This changes these blunt ends into several narrow tips that reduce eddies and drag (4).

[8] Airplane designers have adopted many of these features. The curvature of wings gives lift. Various flaps and projections serve to control airflow or to act as braking devices. Some small planes lessen wing-tip drag by the mounting of flat plates at right angles to the wing surface. Airplane wings, however, still fall short of the engineering marvels found in the wings of birds.

[9] ANTIFREEZE. Humans use glycol in car radiators as antifreeze. But certain microscopic plants use chemically similar glycerol to keep from freezing in Antarctic lakes. It is also found in insects that survive in temperatures of 4 degrees below zero Fahrenheit. There are fish that produce their own antifreeze, enabling them to live in the frigid waters of Antarctica. Some trees survive temperatures of 40 degrees below zero Fahrenheit because

---

9. What animals and plants preceded man in the use of antifreeze, and how effective is it?

they contain "very pure water, without dust or dirt particles upon which ice crystals can form."[4]

¹⁰ UNDERWATER BREATHING. People strap tanks of air to their backs and remain under water for up to an hour. Certain water beetles do it more simply and stay under longer. They grab a bubble of air and submerge. The bubble serves as a lung. It takes carbon dioxide from the beetle and diffuses it into the water, and takes oxygen dissolved in the water for the beetle to use.

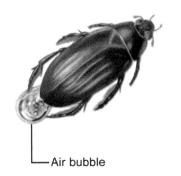

—Air bubble

¹¹ CLOCKS. Long before people used sundials, clocks in living organisms were keeping accurate time. When the tide is out microscopic plants called diatoms come to the surface of wet beach sand. When the tide comes in the diatoms go down into the sand again. Yet in sand in the laboratory, without any tidal ebb and flow, their clocks still make them come up and go down in time with the tides. Fiddler crabs turn a darker color and come out during low tide, turn pale and retreat to their burrows during high tide. In the laboratory away from the ocean, they still keep time with the changing tide, turning dark and light as the tide ebbs and flows. Birds can navigate by sun and stars, which change position as time passes. They must have internal clocks to compensate for these changes. (Jeremiah 8:7) From microscopic plants to people, millions of internal clocks are ticking away.

¹² COMPASSES. About the 13th century C.E. men began to use a magnetic needle floating in a bowl of water—a crude compass. But it was nothing new. Bacteria contain strings of magnetite particles just the right size to make a compass. These guide them to their preferred environments. Magnetite has been found in many other organisms

10. How do certain water beetles make and use underwater breathing devices?
11. How extensive are biological clocks in nature, and what are some examples?
12. When did men start using crude compasses, but how were they in use long before this?

155

—birds, bees, butterflies, dolphins, mollusks and others. Experiments indicate that homing pigeons can return home by sensing the earth's magnetic field. It is now generally accepted that one of the ways migrating birds find their way is by the magnetic compasses in their heads.

[13] DESALINATION. Men build huge factories to remove salt from seawater. Mangrove trees have roots that suck up seawater, but filter it through membranes that remove the salt. One species of mangrove, *Avicennia,* using glands on the underside of its leaves, gets rid of the excess salt. Sea birds, such as gulls, pelicans, cormorants, albatross and petrels, drink seawater and by means of glands in their heads remove the excess salt that gets into their blood. Also penguins, sea turtles and sea iguanas drink salt water, removing the excess salt.

[14] ELECTRICITY. Some 500 varieties of electric fish have batteries. The African catfish can produce 350 volts. The giant electric ray of the North Atlantic puts out 50-ampere pulses of 60 volts. Shocks from the South American electric eel have been measured as high as 886 volts. "Eleven different families of fishes are known to include species with electrical organs," a chemist says.[5]

[15] FARMING. For ages men have tilled the soil and tended livestock. But long before that, leaf-cutting ants were gardeners. For food they grew fungi in a compost they had made from leaves and their droppings. Some ants keep aphids as livestock, milk sugary honeydew from them and even build barns to shelter them. Harvester ants store seeds in underground granaries. (Proverbs 6:6-8) A beetle prunes mimosa trees. Pikas and marmots cut, cure and store hay.

---

13. (a) How are mangroves able to live in salt water? (b) What animals can drink seawater, and how so?
14. What are some examples of creatures that generate electricity?
15. Animals conduct what various farming activities?

¹⁶ INCUBATORS. Man makes incubators to hatch eggs, but in this he is a latecomer. Sea turtles and some birds lay their eggs in the warm sand for incubation. Other birds will lay their eggs in the warm ashes of volcanoes for hatching. Sometimes alligators will cover their eggs with decaying vegetable matter to produce heat. But in this the male mallee bird is the expert. He digs a big hole, fills it with vegetable matter and covers it with sand. The fermenting vegetation heats the mound, the female mallee bird lays an egg in it weekly for up to six months, and all that time the male checks the temperature by sticking his beak into the mound. By adding or removing sand, even in weather from below freezing to very hot, he keeps his incubator at 92 degrees Fahrenheit.

¹⁷ JET PROPULSION. Today when you fly in a plane you are probably being jet-propelled. Many animals are also jet-propelled and have been for millenniums. Both the octopus and the squid excel in this. They suck water into a special chamber and then, with powerful muscles, expel it, shooting themselves forward. Also using jet propulsion: the chambered nautilus, scallops, jellyfish, dragonfly larvae and even some oceanic plankton.

¹⁸ LIGHTING. Thomas Edison is credited with inventing the light bulb. But it is not too efficient, as it loses energy in the form of heat. Fireflies do better as they flash their lights on and off. They produce cold light that loses no energy. Many sponges, fungi, bacteria and worms glow brightly. One, called the railroad worm, is like a miniature train moving along with its red "headlight" and 11 white or pale green pairs of "windows." Many fish

16. (a) How do sea turtles, some birds and alligators incubate their eggs? (b) Why is the male mallee bird's job a most challenging one, and how does he do it?
17. How do the octopus and the squid use jet propulsion, and what unrelated animals also use it?
18. What are some of the many plants and animals that have lights, and in what way are their lights more efficient than man's?

have lights: flashlight fish, anglerfish, lantern fish, viperfish and constellation fish, to name a few. Microorganisms in the ocean surf light up and sparkle by the millions.

[19] PAPER. Egyptians made it thousands of years ago. Even so, they were far behind wasps, yellow jackets and hornets. These winged workers chew up weathered wood, producing a gray paper to make their nests. Hornets hang their large round nests from a tree. The outer covering is many layers of tough paper, separated by dead-air spaces. This insulates the nest from heat and cold as effectively as would a brick wall 16 inches thick.

[20] ROTARY ENGINE. Microscopic bacteria preceded man by thousands of years in making a rotary engine. One bacterium has hairlike extensions twisted together to form a stiff spiral, like a corkscrew. It spins this corkscrew around like the propeller of a ship and drives itself forward. It can even reverse its engine! But how it works is not completely understood. One report claims that the bacterium can attain speeds equivalent to 30 miles an hour, and it says that "nature had, in effect, invented the wheel."[6] A researcher concludes: "One of the most fantastic concepts in biology has come true: Nature has indeed produced a rotary engine, complete with coupling, rotating axle, bearings, and rotating power transmission."[7]

[21] SONAR. The sonar of bats and dolphins surpasses man's copy of it. In a darkened room with fine wires strung across it, bats fly about and never touch the wires. Their supersonic sound signals bounce off these objects and return to the bats, who then make use of echolocation to avoid them. Porpoises and whales do the same thing in water.

19. Who made paper long before man, and how does one papermaker insulate its home?
20. How does one type of bacterium move about, and how have scientists reacted to this?
21. How do several animals, completely unrelated, use sonar?

Oilbirds use echolocation as they enter and leave the dark caves they roost in, making sharp clicking sounds to guide them.

[22] SUBMARINES. Many submarines existed before men invented them. Microscopic radiolarians have oil droplets in their protoplasm by which they regulate their weight and thereby move up or down in the ocean. Fish diffuse gas in to or out of their swim bladders, altering their buoyancy. Inside its shell, the chambered nautilus has chambers or flotation tanks. By altering the proportions of water and gas in these tanks, it regulates its depth. The cuttlebone (the calcified internal shell) of the cuttlefish is filled with cavities. To control buoyancy, this octopuslike creature pumps water out of its skeleton and allows gas to fill the emptied cavity. Thus the cavities of the cuttlebone function just like water tanks in a submarine.

Cross section of chambered nautilus

[23] THERMOMETERS. From the 17th century onward men have developed thermometers, but they are crude compared to some found in nature. A mosquito's antennae can sense a change of 1/300 degree Fahrenheit. A rattlesnake has pits on the sides of its head with which it can sense a change of 1/600 degree Fahrenheit. A boa constrictor responds in 35 milliseconds to a heat change of a fraction of a degree. The beaks of the mallee bird and the brush turkey can tell temperature to within one degree Fahrenheit.

[24] All this copying from animals by humans is reminiscent of what the Bible suggests: "Ask the very beasts, and they will teach you; ask the wild birds—they will tell you; crawling creatures will instruct you, fish in the sea will inform you."—Job 12:7, 8, *Moffatt.*

---

22. How does the principle of ballast that is used in submarines work in several different, unrelated animals?
23. What animals use heat-sensing organs, and how accurate are they?
24. What expression do these examples remind us of?

Chapter 13

Instinct—Wisdom
Programmed Before Birth

Darwin: "I have nothing to do with the origin of the mental powers"

"MANY instincts are so wonderful that their development will probably appear to the reader a difficulty sufficient to overthrow my whole theory," Darwin wrote. He evidently felt that instinct was an unanswerable difficulty, for his next sentence was: "I may here premise that I have nothing to do with the origin of the mental powers, any more than I have with that of life itself."[1]

[2] Scientists today are no closer to explaining instinct than Darwin was. One evolutionist says: "The plain fact is that the genetic mechanism shows not the slightest sign of being able to convey specific behaviour patterns. . . . When we ask ourselves how any instinctive pattern of behaviour arose in the first place *and became hereditarily fixed* we are given no answer."[2]

As to how instinct arose and became hereditary, "we are given no answer"

[3] Yet one widely circulated book on birds, unlike Darwin and other evolutionists, sees no difficulty in accounting for one of the most mysterious instincts —that involved in migration. It says: "There is no question that the process has been an evolutionary

1. What were Darwin's comments about instinct?
2. How do some scientists today view instinct?
3, 4. What does one book have to say about how the instinct to migrate got started, and how does its explanation fall short?

160

one: birds originating in warm climates probably spread outward in their search for food."[3]

[4] Can such a simplistic answer explain the astounding feats of many migrators? Scientists know that any such experimental wanderings and learned behaviors are not incorporated into the genetic code and hence are not inherited by the offspring. Migration is admittedly instinctive and "independent of past experience."[4] Consider a few examples.

The arctic tern migrates 22,000 miles every year

Awesome Feats of Migrators

[5] The long-distance champions are the arctic terns. Nesting north of the Arctic Circle, at summer's end they fly south to spend the Antarctic summer on the pack ice near the South Pole. They may circle the entire continent of Antarctica before heading north to return to the Arctic. They thus complete an annual migration of about 22,000 miles. Rich food sources are available at both polar regions, so one scientist raises the question: "How did they ever discover that such sources existed so far apart?"[5] Evolution has no answer.

[6] Just as unexplainable for evolution is the migration of the blackpoll warbler. It weighs only three quarters of an ounce. Yet in the fall it travels from Alaska to the eastern coast of Canada or New England, gorges on food, stores up fat and then waits for a cold front. When it comes, the bird takes off. Its final destination is South America, but it first heads toward Africa. Out over the Atlantic Ocean, flying at an altitude of up to some 20,000 feet, it picks up a prevailing wind that turns it toward South America.

[7] How does the warbler know to wait for the cold front, and that it means good weather and a tail

How does this warbler with a brain the size of a pea know so much about weather and navigation?

5. What migrations make the arctic terns the long-distance champions, and what question is raised by one scientist?
6, 7. What seems strange about the blackpoll warbler's migration, and what questions make us realize the magnitude of its performance?

When migrating, this hummingbird beats its wings up to 75 times a second for 25 hours

wind? How does it know to climb higher and higher, where air is thin and cold, and has 50 percent less oxygen? How does it know that only up that high does the crosswind blow that will carry it to South America? How does it know to fly toward Africa to allow for the southwestern drift from this wind? The blackpoll does not consciously know any of these things. On this trip of some 2,400 miles, over trackless seas, flying for three or four days and nights, it is governed by instinct alone.

[8] White storks summer in Europe but fly 8,000 miles to winter in South Africa. The golden plover travels from the Arctic tundra to the pampas in Argentina. Certain sandpipers migrate a thousand miles beyond the pampas to the tip of South America. Bristle-thighed curlews fly from Alaska to Tahiti and other islands, up to 6,000 miles over open ocean. In a much shorter flight but just as remarkable, considering its size, the tenth-of-an-ounce ruby-throated hummingbird in its migration of 600 miles crosses the Gulf of Mexico, beating its tiny wings up to 75 times a second for 25 hours. Over six million wingbeats without stopping!

[9] Many migrations are made for the first time by young birds without adults. Young long-tailed cuckoos of New Zealand travel 4,000 miles to Pacific islands to join their parents who had gone earlier. Manx shearwaters migrate from Wales to Brazil, leaving behind their chicks, which follow them as soon as they can fly. One made the trip in 16 days, averaging 460 miles per day. A Manx shearwater was taken from Wales to Boston, far off its normal migratory route. Yet it returned to its home burrow in Wales 3,200 miles away in 12 1/2 days. Homing pigeons, taken 625 miles away in any direction, have returned to their home lofts in one day.

Born with a "map" in their heads, migrating birds know where they are and where they are going

8. What additional migratory feats are here mentioned?
9. (a) What shows that abilities to migrate are not learned but must be programmed before birth? (b) What experiments with a Manx shearwater and with homing pigeons show that these birds are versatile navigators?

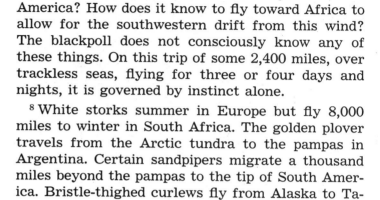

[10] One last example: birds that do not fly but walk and swim. Consider the Adélie penguins. When removed 1,200 miles from their rookeries and released, they quickly oriented themselves and set out in a straight line, not for the home rookery from which they were taken, but for the open sea and food. From the sea they eventually returned to the rookery. They spend the almost totally dark winters at sea. But how do the penguins stay oriented during the dark winter? No one knows.

[11] How do birds perform these feats of navigation? Experiments indicate that they may use the sun and the stars. They appear to have internal clocks to compensate for the movement of these heavenly bodies. But what if the sky is overcast? At least some birds have built-in magnetic compasses for use then. But more than a compass direction is needed. They need a "map" in their heads, with both starting and destination points on it. And on the map the route must be marked, since it is seldom a straight line. *But none of this helps unless they know where they are located on the map!* The Manx shearwater had to know where it was when released in Boston to determine the direction to Wales. The homing pigeon had to know where it had been taken before it could ascertain the way to its loft.

[12] As late as the Middle Ages the fact of widespread bird migration was disputed by many, but the Bible spoke of it in the sixth century B.C.E.: "The stork in the sky knows the time to migrate, the dove and the swift and the wryneck know the season of return." By now much has been learned, but much is still a mystery. Like it or not, what the

Penguins can spend months at sea in almost total darkness and then migrate unerringly back to their rookeries

---

10. What experiment showed the Adélie penguins' powers of navigation?
11. What is required for birds to perform such amazing feats of navigation?
12. (a) What did Jeremiah say about migration, when did he say it, and why is this remarkable? (b) Why may we never know all the details about migration?

Nest Building and Instinct

"There is not the faintest indication," says science writer G. R. Taylor concerning the genetic machinery, "that it can hand on a behavioural programme of a specific kind, such as the sequence of actions involved in nest building."[a] Nevertheless, the instinctive wisdom of nest building *is* handed down, not taught. Consider a few examples.

Hornbills of Africa and Asia. The female brings clay and walls up the opening to a cavity in a hollow tree until she can just barely squeeze inside. The male brings her more mud and she closes the hole until only a slit remains open. Through it the male feeds her, and the babies that eventually hatch. When the male can no longer bring enough food, the female breaks out. This time the opening is repaired by the babies, and both parents bring food to them. Several weeks later, the babies break down the wall and leave the nest. Incidentally, is it not an evidence of purposeful design for the female, while confined and not flying, to molt completely and grow a new wardrobe of feathers?

Swifts. One species makes its nests out of saliva. Before the breeding season begins, the salivary glands swell and produce a viscous, mucous secretion. With its arrival comes the instinctive wisdom to know what to do with it. They smear it on a rock face; as it hardens more layers are added, and finally a cup-shaped nest is completed. Another species of swifts makes nests no bigger than a teaspoon, glues them on to palm leaves and then glues the eggs in the nest.

Emperor Penguins carry built-in nests. In the Antarctic winter the female lays an egg and goes off fishing for two or three months. The male puts the egg on his feet, which are richly supplied with blood vessels, and drapes over it a brood pouch that hangs down from his abdomen. Mother does not forget father and baby. Soon after the egg hatches, the mother returns with a stomach full of food that she regurgitates for them. Then the male goes off to fish while mother puts baby on her feet and drapes her brood pouch over it.

The Weaverbirds of Africa use grasses and other fibers to make their hanging nests. They instinctively use a variety of weave patterns and various kinds of knots. Sociable weavers build what may be likened to apartment houses, making a thatched roof some 15 feet in diameter in strong tree branches, and to the bottom of this, many pairs attach their nests. New nests are added until over a hundred nests may eventually be sheltered under the one roof.

The Tailorbird of southern Asia makes thread from cotton or bark fibers and spiderweb, splicing short pieces together to make longer lengths. With its beak it punches holes along the two edges of a large leaf. Then, using its beak as a needle, with the thread it pulls the two edges of the leaf together, as we lace up our shoes. When it comes to the end of the thread it either knots it to hold it fast or it splices on a new piece and continues sewing. In this way the tailorbird turns the big leaf into a cup in which it makes the nest.

The Penduline Tit's hanging nest becomes almost like felt because it uses pieces of downy plant material as well as grasses. The basic structure of the nest is made by weaving longer grass fibers back and forth. The bird pushes the ends of the fibers through the mesh with its bill. Then it takes the shorter fibers of downy material and pushes these into the weaving. The process is somewhat like the technique of Oriental carpet weavers. These nests are so strong and soft that they have been used as purses or even as slippers for children.

The Horned Coot usually builds its nest on a small, flat island. However, where it lives this type of island is very rare. So, the horned coot makes its own island! It picks out an appropriate place on the water and then begins to carry stones there in its beak. The stones are piled up in water that is about two or three feet deep, until an island is formed. The base may be as much as 13 feet in diameter, and the pile of stones may weigh more than a ton. On this stone island the horned coot then brings vegetation to build its large nest.

Bible says is true: "He has given men a sense of time past and future, but no comprehension of God's work from beginning to end."—Jeremiah 8:7; Ecclesiastes 3:11, *The New English Bible.*

Other Navigators

[13] Caribou in Alaska migrate south 800 miles in winter. Many whales travel over 6,000 miles from the Arctic Ocean and back. Fur seals migrate between the Pribilof Islands and southern California, 3,000 miles apart. Green sea turtles navigate from the coast of Brazil to tiny Ascension Island, 1,400 miles out in the Atlantic Ocean, and then back. Some crabs migrate up to 150 miles on the ocean floor. Salmon leave the streams where they hatched and spend a few years in the open ocean, then return hundreds of miles to the very same streams of their birth. Young eels born in the Sargasso Sea in the Atlantic spend most of their lives in freshwater streams in the United States and in Europe, but return to the Sargasso Sea to spawn.

[14] Monarch butterflies leave Canada in the fall, many wintering in California or Mexico. Some flights exceed 2,000 miles; one butterfly covered 80 miles in a day. They settle on sheltered trees—the same groves, even the same trees, year after year. But not the same butterflies! On the return trip in spring they deposit eggs on milkweed plants. The new butterflies thus produced continue the northward migration, and in the following fall they make the same 2,000-mile trip south that their parents did, blanketing the same groves of trees. The book *The Story of Pollination* comments: "The butterflies that come south in the fall are young individuals which have never before seen the hibernation sites. What enables them to find these is still one of those elusive mysteries of Nature."[6]

After their 2,000-mile journey south, monarch butterflies rest in their wintering grounds

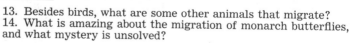

13. Besides birds, what are some other animals that migrate?
14. What is amazing about the migration of monarch butterflies, and what mystery is unsolved?

166

15 Instinctive wisdom is not limited to migration. A quick sampling proves this point.

How can millions of blind termites synchronize their labors to build and air-condition their elaborate structures? *Instinct*.

How does the pronuba moth know the several steps to take to cross-pollinate the yucca flower, whereby both new yucca plants and new moths can be formed? *Instinct*.

How can the spider that lives in its "diving bell" under water know that when the oxygen is gone it must cut a hole in its underwater bell, release the stale air, mend the hole and bring down a new supply of fresh air? *Instinct*.

How does the mimosa girdler beetle know it must lay its eggs under the bark of a mimosa tree branch, come in a foot or so toward the trunk and cut the bark all the way around to kill the branch, because its eggs will not hatch in live wood? *Instinct*.

How does the bean-sized baby kangaroo, born blind and undeveloped, know that to survive it must struggle up unassisted through its mother's fur to her abdomen and into her pouch and attach itself to one of her teats? *Instinct*.

"They are instinctively wise"

How does one dancing honeybee tell other bees where nectar is, how much there is, how far it is, in what direction it is and the kind of flower it is on? *Instinct*.

16 Such questions could continue and fill a book, yet all the questions would have the same answer: "They are instinctively wise." (Proverbs 30:24) "How was it possible," one researcher wonders, "for such complicated instinctive knowledge to develop and be passed on to successive generations?"[7] Men cannot explain it. Evolution cannot account for it. But such intelligence still demands an intelligent source. Such wisdom still calls for a wise source. It calls for an intelligent, wise Creator.

17 Yet many who believe in evolution automatically reject as irrelevant all such evidence for creation, saying it is not a matter for scientific consideration. However, do not let this narrow approach keep you from weighing the evidence. There is more in the following chapter.

___

15. What one word answers several questions on the wisdom of animals?
16. What does all the wisdom behind animal behavior require?
17. What reasoning of many evolutionists is it wise to avoid?

Chapter 14

The Human Miracle

OF ALL the marvelous things on earth, none is more astounding than the human brain. For example, every second some 100 million bits of information pour into the brain from the various senses. But how can it avoid being hopelessly buried by this avalanche? If we can think about only one thing at a time, how does the mind cope with these millions of simultaneous messages? Obviously, the mind not only survives the barrage but handles it with ease.

How can the brain cope with 100 million messages pouring into it every second?

[2] How it does so is only one of the many wonders of the human brain. Two factors are involved. First, in the brain stem there is a network of nerves the size of your little finger. This network is called the reticular formation. It acts as a kind of traffic control center, monitoring the millions of messages coming into the brain, sifting out the trivial and selecting the essential for attention by the cerebral cortex. Each second this little network of nerves

1. What fact about the brain would seem to present a major problem for it?
2, 3. In what two ways does the brain cope with this problem?

permits only a few hundred, at most, to enter the conscious mind.

[3] Second, a further pinpointing of our attention seems to come about by waves that sweep the brain 8 to 12 times per second. These waves cause periods of high sensitivity, during which the brain notes the stronger signals and acts upon them. It is believed that by means of these waves the brain scans itself, in this way focusing on the essentials. Thus an amazing flurry of activity is going on in our heads every second!

The brain scans itself about every tenth of a second to focus on the essentials

Something "to Wonder At"

[4] In recent years scientists have made tremendous strides in studies of the brain. Even so, what they have learned is nothing compared to what remains unknown. One researcher said that, after thousands of years of speculation and recent decades of intensive scientific research, our brains, along with the universe, remain "essentially mysterious."[1] Certainly the human brain is easily the most mysterious part of the human miracle —"miracle" meaning something "to wonder at."

[5] The wonder begins in the womb. Three weeks after conception brain cells start forming. They grow in spurts, at times up to 250,000 cells a minute. After birth the brain continues growing and forming its network of connections. The gulf separating the human brain from that of any animal quickly manifests itself: "The brain of the human infant, unlike that of any other animal, triples in size during its first year," states the book *The Universe Within.*[2] In time, about 100 billion nerve cells, called neurons, as well as other types of cells, are packed into a human brain, although it makes up only 2 percent of the body's weight.

Our brains remain "essentially mysterious"

4. In spite of intensive scientific research to understand the brain, what still remains true?
5. What fact about the development of the human brain in a growing infant shows the gulf between it and the brains of animals?

Dendrites

Neuron

Axon

Synapse

Neuron

Axon

The brain, like a muscle, is strengthened by use and weakened by disuse

[6] The key brain cells—the neurons—do not actually touch one another. They are separated by synapses, tiny spaces less than one millionth of an inch across. These gaps are bridged by chemicals called neurotransmitters, 30 of which are known, but the brain may possess many more. These chemical signals are received at one end of the neuron by a maze of tiny filaments called dendrites. The signals are then transmitted at the other end of the neuron by a nerve fiber called an axon. In the neurons the signals are electrical, but across the gaps they are chemical. Thus the transmission of nerve signals is electrochemical in nature. Each impulse is of the same strength, but the intensity of the signal depends upon the frequency of the impulses, which may be as high as one thousand a second.

[7] It is not certain just what physiological changes take place in the brain when we learn. But experimental evidence suggests that as we learn, especially in early life, better connections are formed, and more of the chemicals bridging the gaps between neurons are released. Continued use strengthens the connections, and thus learning is reinforced. "Pathways that are often activated together are strengthened in some way," reports *Scientific American*.[3] Interesting on this point is the Bible's comment that deeper matters are more easily understood by mature people "who through *use* have their perceptive powers trained." (Hebrews 5:14) Research has revealed that unused mental powers fade away. Thus the brain, like a muscle, is strengthened by use and weakened by disuse.

[8] The vast numbers of microscopic nerve fibers making these connections within the brain are often referred to as its "wiring." They are precisely placed within a maze of staggering complexity. But

6. How do nerve signals flow from neuron to neuron?
7. What feature of the brain has the Bible commented on, and what have scientists learned that agrees with this?
8. What is one of the great unresolved issues concerning the brain?

170

THE HUMAN BRAIN

"The human brain is the most marvelous and mysterious object in the whole universe."—Anthropologist Henry F. Osborn[a]

"How does the brain produce thoughts? That is the central question and we have still no answer to it."—Physiologist Charles Sherrington[b]

"In spite of the steady accumulation of detailed knowledge how the human brain works is still profoundly mysterious."—Biologist Francis Crick[c]

"Anyone who speaks of a computer as an 'electronic brain' has never seen a brain."—Science editor Dr. Irving S. Bengelsdorf[d]

"Our active memories hold several *billion* times more information than a large contemporary research computer."—Science writer Morton Hunt[e]

"Since the brain is different and immeasurably more complicated than anything else in the known universe, we may have to change some of our most ardently held ideas before we're able to fathom the brain's mysterious structure."—Neurologist Richard M. Restak[f]

Regarding the huge gulf between humans and animals, Alfred R. Wallace, the 'co-discoverer of evolution,' wrote to Darwin: "Natural selection could only have endowed the savage with a brain a little superior to that of the ape, whereas he possesses one very little inferior to that of an average member of our learned society." Darwin, upset by this admission, replied: "I hope you have not murdered completely your own and my child"[g]

To say that the human brain evolved from that of any animal is to defy reason and the facts. Far more logical is this conclusion: "I am left with no choice but to acknowledge the existence of a Superior Intellect, responsible for the design and development of the incredible brain-mind relationship—something far beyond man's capacity to understand. . . . I have to believe all this had an intelligent beginning, that Someone made it happen."—Neurosurgeon Dr. Robert J. White[h]

An 'Unsolved Mystery'?

The brain could hold information that "would fill some twenty million volumes"

how they are placed in the exact spots called for by the "wiring diagrams" is a mystery. "Undoubtedly the most important unresolved issue in the development of the brain," one scientist said, "is the question of how neurons make specific patterns of connections. . . . Most of the connections seem to be precisely established at an early stage of development."[4] Another researcher adds that these specifically mapped-out areas of the brain "are common throughout the nervous system, and how this precise wiring is laid down remains one of the great unsolved problems."[5]

[9] The number of these connections is astronomical! Each neuron may have thousands of connections with other neurons. Not only are there connections between neurons, but there are also microcircuits that are set up directly between the dendrites themselves. "These 'microcircuits,'" says one neurologist, "add a totally new dimension to our already mind-boggling conception of how the brain works."[6] Some researchers believe that the "billions upon billions of nerve cells in the human brain make perhaps as many as a quadrillion connections."[7] With what capacity? Carl Sagan states that the brain could hold information that "would fill some twenty million volumes, as many as in the world's largest libraries."[8]

[10] It is the cerebral cortex of the brain that sets man far apart from any animal. It is less than a quarter of an inch thick, and it forms a fissured mold snug against the skull. If laid out, the cortex would measure about two and a half square feet, with some ten thousand miles of connecting fibers per cubic inch. The human cortex not only is far bigger than that of any animal, but it also has a much larger uncommitted area. That is to say, it is

9. How many connections do scientists estimate exist within the brain, and what does one authority say as to its capacity?
10. (a) In what ways does man's cerebral cortex differ from that of animals, and with what advantages to man? (b) What did one researcher say about this?

172

not committed to handling the physical functions of the body but is free for the higher mental processes that separate people from animals. "We are not just smarter apes," one researcher said. Our minds "make us qualitatively different from all other forms of life."[9]

Our Far Greater Capability

[11] "What distinguishes the human brain," a scientist said, "is the variety of more specialized activities it is capable of learning."[10] Computer science uses the term "hardwired" to refer to built-in characteristics based on fixed circuitry, in contrast to functions put into a computer by a programmer. "Applied to human beings," one authority writes, "hard wiring refers to innate abilities or, at least, predispositions."[11] In people there are many built-in capacities for learning, but not the learning itself. Animals, by contrast, have hardwired instinctive wisdom, but limited capacities to learn new things.

[12] *The Universe Within* notes that the most intelligent animal "never develops a mind like that of a human being. For it lacks what we have: preprogramming of our neural equipment that enables us to form concepts out of what we see, language out of what we hear, and thoughts out of our experiences." But we must, by input from our surroundings, program the brain, otherwise, as the book states, "nothing resembling the human mind would develop . . . Without that immense infusion of experience, scarcely a trace of intellect would appear."[12] So the capability that is built into the human brain enables us to construct the human intellect. And, unlike animals, we have the free will to program our intellects as we choose, based on our own knowledge, values, opportunities and goals.

"We are not just smarter apes." Our minds "make us qualitatively different from all other forms of life"

---

11. How does the human brain give man a flexibility in learning that animals do not have?
12. In contrast to animals, with what capability are human brains preprogrammed, and what freedom does this grant people?

173

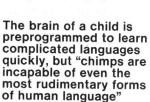

The brain of a child is preprogrammed to learn complicated languages quickly, but "chimps are incapable of even the most rudimentary forms of human language"

Language Unique to Humans

[13] An outstanding example of hardwired capabilities with great flexibility for programming by us is language. Specialists agree that "the human brain is genetically programmed for language development,"[13] and that speech "can be explained only on the basis of an innate language-processing capacity within our brain."[14] Unlike the rigidity that is displayed in the instinctive behavior of animals, however, there is tremendous flexibility in a human's use of this hardwired capacity for language.

[14] A specific language is not hardwired into our brains, but we are preprogrammed with the capacity for learning languages. If two languages are spoken in the home, a child can learn both. If exposed to a third language, the child can learn it also. One girl was exposed to a number of languages from babyhood. By the time she was five she spoke eight fluently. In view of such innate abilities it is no surprise that a linguist said that chimpanzee experiments with sign language "actually prove that chimps are incapable of even the most rudimentary forms of human language."[15]

13, 14. (a) What example of preprogramming leaves great flexibility for people to program into their intellect whatever they choose? (b) In view of this, what did one noted linguist say about animals and language?

174

[15] Could such an amazing ability have evolved from the grunts and growls of animals? Studies of the most ancient languages rule out any such evolution of language. One specialist said that "there are no primitive languages."[16] Anthropologist Ashley Montagu agreed that so-called primitive languages "are often a great deal more complex and more efficient than the languages of the so-called higher civilizations."[17]

[16] One neurologist concludes: "The more we attempt to investigate the mechanism of language, the more mysterious the process becomes."[18] Another researcher says: "At present the origin of syntactic speech remains a mystery."[19] And a third states: "The power of speech, moving men and nations as no other force, uniquely sets humans apart from animals. Yet, the origins of language remain one of the brain's most baffling mysteries."[20] It is no mystery, however, to those who see in it the hand of a Creator who "hardwired" areas in the brain for language capabilities.

"The origins of language remain one of the brain's most baffling mysteries"

Things Only Creation Can Explain

[17] The *Encyclopædia Britannica* states that man's brain "is endowed with considerably more potential than is realizable in the course of one person's lifetime."[21] It also has been stated that the human brain could take any load of learning and memory put on it now, and a billion times that! But why would evolution produce such an excess? "This is, in fact, the only example in existence where a species was provided with an organ that it still has not learned how to use," admitted one scientist. He then asked: "How can this be reconciled with evolution's

The human brain's development "remains the most inexplicable aspect of evolution"

15. What does science show relative to the most ancient languages?
16. What do some researchers say about the origin of language, yet to whom is it no mystery?
17. (a) What fact about the brain presents evolution with an inexplicable problem? (b) What would make it logical for man to have such a tremendous brain capacity?

most fundamental thesis: Natural selection proceeds in small steps, each of which must confer on its bearer a minimal, but nonetheless measurable, advantage?" He added that the human brain's development "remains the most inexplicable aspect of evolution."[22] Since the evolutionary process would not produce and pass on such excessive never-to-be-used brain capacity, is it not more reasonable to conclude that man, with the capacity for endless learning, was designed to live forever?

[18] Carl Sagan, amazed that the human brain could hold information that "would fill some twenty million volumes," stated: "The brain is a very big place in a very small space."[23] And what happens in this small space defies human understanding. For example, imagine what must be going on in the brain of a pianist playing a difficult musical composition, with all fingers flying over the keys. What an astonishing sense of movement his brain must have, to order the fingers to strike the right keys at the right time with the right force to match the notes in his head! And if he hits a wrong note, the brain immediately lets him know about it! All this incredibly complex operation has been programmed into his brain by years of practice. But it is made possible only because musical capability was pre-programmed into the human brain from birth.

[19] No animal brain ever conceived such things, much less is able to do them. Nor does any evolutionary theory provide an explanation. Is it not evident that man's intellectual qualities mirror those of a Supreme Intellect? This harmonizes with Genesis 1:27, which states: "God proceeded to create the man in his image." The animals were not created in God's image. That is why they do not have the capabilities man has. Though animals do

Humans have capabilities far beyond those of any animal

18. What was one scientist's summation of the human brain, and what shows its capabilities?
19. What explains the intellectual qualities and other marvelous abilities possessed by the human brain?

176

amazing things by predetermined, rigid instincts, they are no match at all for humans with their flexibility in thinking and acting and their ability to continually build on previous knowledge.

[20] The human capacity for altruism—unselfish giving—creates another problem for evolution. As one evolutionist noted: "Anything that has evolved by natural selection should be selfish." And many humans are selfish, of course. But as he later acknowledged: "It is possible that yet another unique quality of man is a capacity for genuine, disinterested, true altruism."[24] Another scientist added: "Altruism is built into us."[25] Only in humans is it practiced with an awareness of the cost, or sacrifice, that may be involved.

Appreciating the Human Miracle

[21] Just consider: Man originates abstract thinking, consciously sets goals, makes plans to reach them, initiates work to carry them out and finds satisfaction in their accomplishment. Created with an eye for beauty, an ear for music, a flair for art, an urge to learn, an insatiable curiosity, and an imagination that invents and creates—man finds joy and fulfillment in exercising these gifts. He is challenged by problems, and delights in using his mental and physical powers to solve them. A moral sense to determine right and wrong and a conscience to prick him when he strays—these too man has. He finds happiness in giving, and joy in loving and being loved. All such activities enhance his pleasure in living and give purpose and meaning to his life.

Man's awesome brain bears the "image" of the One who made him

[22] A human can contemplate the plants and animals, the grandeur of the mountains and oceans around him, the vastness of the starry heavens

---

20. In what way is man's altruism inconsistent with evolution?
21. What abilities and qualities of man remove him far beyond any animal?
22. What contemplations make man feel his smallness and cause him to grope for understanding?

"In your book all its parts were down in writing"

above him, and feel his smallness. He is aware of time and eternity, wonders how he got here and where he is going, and gropes to understand what is behind it all. No animal entertains such thoughts. But a human seeks the whys and wherefores of things. All of this results from his being endowed with an awesome brain and his bearing the "image" of the One who made him.

[23] With amazing insight, the ancient psalmist David gave credit to the One who designed the brain and whom he considered to be responsible for the miracle of human birth. He said: "I shall laud you because in a fear-inspiring way I am wonderfully made. Your works are wonderful, as my soul is very well aware. My bones were not hidden from you when I was made in secret, when I was woven in the lowest parts of the earth. Your eyes saw even the embryo of me, and in your book all its parts were down in writing."—Psalm 139:14-16.

[24] Truly, it can be said that the fertilized egg in the mother's womb contains all the parts of the emerging human body "down in writing." The heart, the lungs, the kidneys, the eyes and ears, the arms and legs, and the awesome brain—these and all the other parts of the body were 'written down' in the genetic code of the fertilized egg in the mother's womb. Contained in this code are internal timetables for the appearance of these parts, each one in its proper order. This fact was recorded in the Bible nearly three thousand years before modern science ever discovered the genetic code!

[25] Is not the existence of man with his amazing brain truly a miracle, a cause for wonderment? Is it not also evident that such a miracle can be accounted for only by creation, not evolution?

---

23. How did David give credit for his origin, and what did he say about his formation in the womb?
24. What scientific discoveries make David's words all the more amazing?
25. To what conclusion does all of this lead?

Chapter 15

Why Do Many Accept Evolution?

AS WE have seen, the evidence for creation is enormous. Why, then, do many people reject creation and accept evolution instead? One reason is what they were taught in school. Science textbooks nearly always promote the evolutionary viewpoint. The student is rarely, if ever, exposed to opposing arguments. In fact, arguments against evolution are usually prevented from appearing in school textbooks.

The student is rarely given opposing arguments

[2] In the magazine *American Laboratory* a doctor wrote this about his children's schooling: "The child is not presented with evolution as a theory. Subtle statements are made in science texts as early as the second grade (based on my reading of my children's textbooks). Evolution is presented as reality, not as a concept that can be questioned. The authority of the educational system then compels

1, 2. What is one reason why many people believe evolution?

179

belief." Regarding evolutionary teaching in higher grades, he said: "A student is not permitted to hold personal beliefs or to state them: if the student does so, he or she is subjected to ridicule and criticism by the instructor. Often the student risks academic loss because his or her views are not 'correct' and the grade is lowered."[1]

[3] Evolutionary views permeate not only the schools but all areas of science and other fields such as history and philosophy. Books, magazine articles, motion pictures and television programs treat it as an established fact. Often we hear or read phrases such as, 'When man evolved from the lower animals,' or, 'Millions of years ago, when life evolved in the oceans.' Thus, people are conditioned to accept evolution as a fact, and contrary evidence passes unnoticed.

Evolutionary teaching permeates science and other fields

Weight of Authority

[4] When leading educators and scientists assert that evolution is a fact, and imply that only the ignorant refuse to believe it, how many laymen are going to contradict them? This weight of authority that is brought to bear on evolution's behalf is a major reason for its acceptance by large numbers of people.

[5] An example typical of views that often intimidate laymen is this assertion by Richard Dawkins: "Darwin's theory is now supported by all the available relevant evidence, and its truth is not doubted by any serious modern biologist."[2] But is this actually the case? Not at all. A little research will reveal that many scientists, including 'serious modern biologists,' not only doubt evolution but do not believe it.[3] They believe that the evidence for creation is far, far stronger. Thus, sweeping state-

Many educators and scientists say or imply that only the ignorant disbelieve evolution

3. How are some people conditioned to accept evolution?
4. How is the weight of authority brought to bear on evolution's behalf?
5. (a) What example shows how scientists often use their weight of authority? (b) Why are such assertions in error?

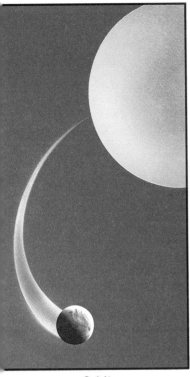

Orbit

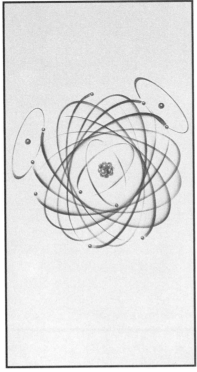

Water

Gravity

ments like that of Dawkins are in error. But they are typical of attempts to bury opposition by means of such language. Noting this, an observer wrote in *New Scientist:* "Does Richard Dawkins have so little faith in the evidence for evolution that he has to make sweeping generalisations in order to dismiss opponents to his beliefs?"[4]

6 In similar fashion the book *A View of Life,* by evolutionists Luria, Gould and Singer, states that "evolution is a fact," and asserts: "We might as well doubt that the earth revolves about the sun, or that hydrogen and oxygen make water."[5] It also declares that evolution is as much a fact as the existence of gravity. But it can be proved experimentally that the earth revolves around the sun, that hydrogen and oxygen make water, and that gravity exists. Evolution cannot be proved experimentally. Indeed, these same evolutionists admit that "debate rages

Do debates still rage about the earth orbiting the sun, about hydrogen and oxygen making water, about gravity's existence?

---

6. How is evolutionary dogmatism contrary to the accepted scientific method?

181

about theories of evolution."[6] But do debates still rage about the earth revolving around the sun, about hydrogen and oxygen making water, and about the existence of gravity? No. How reasonable is it, then, to say that evolution is as much a fact as these things are?

[7] In a foreword to John Reader's book *Missing Links,* David Pilbeam shows that scientists do not always base their conclusions on facts. One reason, says Pilbeam, is that scientists "are also people and because much is at stake, for there are glittering prizes in the form of fame and publicity." The book acknowledges that evolution is "a science powered by individual ambitions and so susceptible to preconceived beliefs." As an example it notes: "When preconception is . . . so enthusiastically welcomed and so long accommodated as in the case of Piltdown Man, science reveals a disturbing predisposition towards belief before investigation." The author adds: "Modern [evolutionists] are no less likely to cling to erroneous data that supports their preconceptions than were earlier investigators . . . [who] dismissed objective assessment in favour of the notions they wanted to believe."[7] So, because of having committed themselves to evolution, and a desire to further their careers, some scientists will not admit the possibility of error. Instead, they work to justify preconceived ideas rather than acknowledge possibly damaging facts.

[8] This unscientific attitude was noted and deplored by W. R. Thompson in his foreword to the centennial edition of Darwin's *The Origin of Species.* Thompson stated: "If arguments fail to resist analysis, assent should be withheld, and a wholesale conversion due to unsound argument must be regarded as deplorable." He said: "The facts and interpretations on which Darwin relied have now

> "[Evolutionary] science reveals a disturbing predisposition towards belief before investigation"

> "The facts and interpretations on which Darwin relied have now ceased to convince"

7. Why do scientists not always base their conclusions on facts?
8. Why did W. R. Thompson deplore the wholesale conversion to belief in evolution?

ceased to convince. The long-continued investigations on heredity and variation have undermined the Darwinian position."[8]

[9] Thompson also observed: "A long-enduring and regrettable effect of the success of the *Origin* was the addiction of biologists to unverifiable speculation. . . . The success of Darwinism was accompanied by a decline in scientific integrity." He concluded: "This situation, where scientific men rally to the defence of a doctrine they are unable to define scientifically, much less demonstrate with scientific rigour, attempting to maintain its credit with the public by the suppression of criticism and the elimination of difficulties, is abnormal and undesirable in science."[9]

[10] Similarly, a professor of anthropology, Anthony Ostric, criticized his scientific colleagues for declaring "as a fact" that man descended from apelike creatures. He said that "at best it is only a hypothesis and not a well-supported one at that." He noted that "there is no evidence that man has not remained essentially the same since the first evidence of his appearance." The anthropologist said that the vast body of professionals have fallen in behind those who promote evolution "for fear of not being declared serious scholars or of being rejected from serious academic circles."[10] In this regard, Hoyle and Wickramasinghe also comment: "You either believe the concepts or you will inevitably be branded as a heretic."[11] One result of this has been an unwillingness by many scientists to investigate the creation viewpoint without prejudice. As a letter to the editor of *Hospital Practice* observed: "Science has always prided itself upon its objectivity, but I'm afraid that we scientists are rapidly becoming victims of the prejudiced, closed-minded thinking that we have so long abhorred."[12]

"The suppression of criticism . . . is abnormal and undesirable in science"

---

9. What did Thompson say about scientists suppressing criticism of evolution?
10. Why do many scientists accept evolution as "fact"?

Clergy backing of both sides in war, intolerance, and false teachings such as hellfire alienate many

Failure of Religion

[11] An additional reason for evolution's acceptance is the failure of conventional religion in both what it teaches and what it does, as well as its failure to represent properly the Bible's creation account. Informed persons are well aware of the religious record of hypocrisy, oppression and inquisitions. They have observed clergy support for murderous dictators. They know that people of the same religion have killed one another by the millions in war, with the clergy backing each side. So they find no reason for considering the God whom those religions are supposed to represent. Too, absurd and unbiblical doctrines further this alienation. Such ideas as eternal torment—that God will roast people in a literal hellfire forever—are repugnant to reasoning persons.

[12] However, not only are reasoning persons re-

11. How has religion's failure been a factor in the acceptance of evolution?
12. What does the failure of this world's religions really show?

184

pelled by such religious teachings and actions, but the evidence in the Bible is that God also is repelled. Indeed, the Bible frankly exposes the hypocrisy of certain religious leaders. For example, it says of them: "You also, outwardly indeed, appear righteous to men, but inside you are full of hypocrisy and lawlessness." (Matthew 23:28) Jesus told the common people that their clergy were "blind guides" who taught, not what comes from God, but contrary "commands of men as doctrines." (Matthew 15:9, 14) Similarly, the Bible condemns religionists who "publicly declare they know God, but [who] disown him by their works." (Titus 1:16) So, despite their claims, religions that have promoted or condoned hypocrisy and bloodshed do not originate with God, nor do they represent him. Instead, they are called "false prophets," and are compared to trees that produce "worthless fruit."—Matthew 7:15-20; John 8:44; 13:35; 1 John 3:10-12.

[13] Also, many religions have capitulated on the matter of evolution, thus providing no alternative for their people. For example, the *New Catholic Encyclopedia* states: "General evolution, even of the body of man, seems the most probable scientific account of origins."[13] At a Vatican meeting, 12 scholars representing the highest scientific body of the Catholic Church agreed to this conclusion: "We are convinced that masses of evidence render the application of the concept of evolution to man and other primates beyond serious dispute."[14] With such religious endorsement, are uninformed church members likely to resist even when, in reality, "masses of evidence" do not support evolution, but, instead, actually support creation?

The vacuum caused by religious error often leads to acceptance of evolution

[14] The vacuum that this causes is often filled by agnosticism and atheism. Abandoning belief in God, people accept evolution as the alternative. Today, in a number of lands, atheism based on evolution is

---

13. What lack of guidance is evident in religion?
14. How is the vacuum caused by false religion often filled?

even the official state policy. Responsibility for much of this disbelief can be laid at the feet of this world's religions.

[15] Too, some religious doctrines cause people to believe that the Bible teaches things contrary to scientific fact, so they reject the God of the Bible. For example, as noted in an earlier chapter, some erroneously claim the Bible teaches that the earth was created in six literal 24-hour days, and that it is only 6,000 years old. But the Bible does not teach these things.

'Seeing Is Believing'

[16] Some people sincerely reject the concept of a Creator because they feel, as it has been said, that 'seeing is believing.' If something cannot be seen or measured in some way, then they may feel that it does not exist. True, in daily life they acknowledge the existence of many things that cannot be seen, such as electricity, magnetism, radio or television waves and gravity. Yet, this does not alter their view, because all these things can still be measured or sensed by some other physical means. But there is no physical way to see or measure a Creator, or God.

[17] However, as we have seen in previous chapters, there is sound reason to believe that an unseen Creator does exist because we can observe the evidence, the physical results of his handiwork. We see it in the technical perfection and intricacy of atomic structure, in the magnificently organized universe, in the unique planet Earth, in the amazing designs of living things and in man's awesome brain. These are effects that must have an adequate cause to account for their existence. Even materialists accept this law of cause and effect in all other

The existence of a Creator is evidenced by "the things made"

15. What other erroneous religious ideas discourage belief in God and the Bible?
16. Why do some people reject the concept of a Creator?
17, 18. (a) What evidence that we can see verifies the existence of an unseen Creator? (b) Why should we not expect to see God?

matters. Why not also regarding the physical universe itself?

[18] On this point, the Bible's simple argument puts it best: "[The Creator's] invisible attributes, that is to say his everlasting power and deity, have been visible, ever since the world began, to the eye of reason, *in the things he has made.*" (Romans 1:20, *The New English Bible*) In other words, the Bible reasons from effect to cause. The visible creation, the awesome "things he has made," are an evident effect that must have an intelligent cause. That invisible cause is God. Too, as the Maker of all the universe, the Creator no doubt possesses power so enormous that humans of flesh and blood should not expect to see God and survive. As the Bible comments: "No man may see [God] and yet live." —Exodus 33:20.

Another Major Reason for Disbelief

[19] There is another major reason why many people abandon belief in God and accept evolution. It is because of the prevalence of suffering. For centuries there has been so much injustice, oppression, crime, war, sickness and death. Many persons do not understand why all these hardships have come upon the human family. They feel that an all-powerful Creator would not have allowed such things. Since these conditions do exist, they feel that God could not exist. Thus, when evolution is presented they accept it as the only choice, often without much investigation.

Because suffering exists, many abandon belief in God and accept evolution

[20] Why, then, would an all-powerful Creator permit so much suffering? Will it forever be this way? Understanding the answer to this problem will, in turn, enable one to understand the deeper, underlying reason for the theory of evolution becoming so widespread in our time.

19. What is another major reason why many accept evolution?
20. What questions need answering?

Chapter 16

Why Would God Permit Suffering?

A COMMON reason many people give for doubting the existence of a Creator is the prevalence of suffering in the world. Throughout the centuries there has been so much cruelty, bloodshed and outright evil, bringing great suffering to millions of innocent people. Thus many ask: 'If there is a God, why does he permit all of this?' Since, as we have seen, the Bible's account best fits the facts about creation, can the Bible also help us to understand why a powerful Creator would permit so much suffering for such a long time?

Many ask: 'If there is a God, why does he permit all of this?'

² The opening chapters of Genesis provide the background for answering this question. They describe the creation of a world without suffering. The first man and woman were put in a paradise setting, a beautiful gardenlike home called Eden, and they were given pleasant and challenging work. Regarding the earth, they were told "to cultivate it and to take care of it." They also had supervision of "the fish of the sea and the flying creatures of the heavens and every living creature that is moving upon the earth."—Genesis 1:28; 2:15.

1. What is a common reason many people give for doubting the existence of a Creator?
2. How does the Bible describe the setting in which the first human pair were placed?

188

³ In addition, since the first humans were created with perfect bodies and perfect minds, they were not defective in any way. Hence, there was no reason for them ever to suffer from sickness, old age or death. Instead, they had the prospect of an endless future in an earthly paradise.—Deuteronomy 32:4.

The first humans had the prospect of living forever on a paradise earth

⁴ The first pair were also told to "be fruitful and become many and fill the earth." As they would bear children, the human family would increase and extend the boundaries of the Paradise so that it would eventually encompass the entire earth. Thus, the human race would be a united family, all living in perfect health on a paradise earth.

The Need to Accept God's Rule

⁵ However, for this harmony to continue, the first human pair had to accept their Creator's right to govern human affairs. That is, they had to accept his sovereignty. Why? First of all, because it was

3. What prospect was placed before Adam and Eve?
4. What was God's purpose for humans and for the earth itself?
5. Why were humans required to accept God's rule?

proper. The maker of anything surely has a right to exercise a measure of control over what he has made. This principle has been reflected in ownership laws for centuries. In addition, humans needed to accept the direction of their Maker because of this crucial fact: They were not designed with the ability to govern themselves successfully apart from their Creator, any more than they could stay alive if they did not eat, drink and breathe. History has proved the Bible correct in saying: "To earthling man his way does not belong. It does not belong to man who is walking even to direct his step." (Jeremiah 10:23) As long as humans stayed within the guidelines set for them by their Creator, life would be continuous, successful and happy.

Humans were not created to govern themselves successfully apart from their Creator

[6] Also, humans were created to be free agents. They were not made to react like robots, or compelled to do certain things primarily out of instinct, as are animals or insects. But this freedom was to be *relative,* not absolute. It was to be exercised responsibly, within the boundaries of God's laws, laws that worked for the common good. Note how the Bible sets out this principle: "Be as free people, and yet holding your freedom, not as a blind for badness, but as slaves of God." (1 Peter 2:16) Without law to govern human interrelations, there would be anarchy, and the lives of all persons would be affected adversely.

Freedom was to be *relative,* not absolute

[7] Thus, while relative freedom is desirable, too much freedom is not. If you give a child too much freedom, it may lead to his playing on a busy street, or putting his hand on a hot stove. Total freedom to make all of our own decisions without considering our Maker's direction can cause all kinds of problems. That was the case with the first humans. They chose to misuse their gift of freedom. They decided, wrongly, to grasp for independence from their Creator and thereby "be like God." They felt

6, 7. (a) What kind of freedom did God grant to humans, and why? (b) What bad choice did the first humans make?

that they could determine for themselves what was right and what was wrong.—Genesis 3:5.

[8] When the first humans pulled away from their Creator's direction, what happened to them is similar to what happens when you pull out the plug of an electric fan. As long as the fan is plugged into a power source, it runs. But when disconnected, it slows down and eventually comes to a dead stop. That is what happened when Adam and Eve pulled away from their Creator, "the source of life." (Psalm 36:9) Since they willfully chose a course of independence from their Maker, he let them learn the full meaning of their choice by leaving them on their own. As a Bible principle states: "If you leave [God] he will leave you." (2 Chronicles 15:2) Without their Creator's sustaining power, a gradual breakdown of mind and body began. In time, they grew old and died.—Genesis 3:19; 5:5.

As a fan slows down and stops when disconnected, so Adam and Eve grew old and died after they pulled away from their source of life

---

8. What happened when Adam and Eve pulled away from God's rule?

⁹ When Adam and Eve chose to be independent of their Maker, they fell from perfection. This was before they had any children. As a result, when they later had children, these reflected what the parents had become—imperfect. So the first humans became like a defective pattern. Everything produced from them was also defective. Hence, we are all born imperfect and inherit the disabilities of aging, sickness and death. This imperfection, along with separation from the Creator and his laws, opened the floodgates of human folly. Thus, mankind's history has been filled with suffering, sorrow, sickness and death.—Psalm 51:5; Romans 5:12.

Meditating on what is wrong can cause one to do the wrong thing

¹⁰ Is this to say that wickedness originated entirely with humans? No, there is more to it. The creation of intelligent creatures was not limited to humans. Already God had created countless spirit creatures in the heavens. (Job 38:4, 7) They too were free agents and also had a choice in accepting their Creator's direction. One of those spirit creatures chose to dwell on a desire for independence. His ambition built up to such a degree that it moved him to challenge God's authority. He told Adam's wife, Eve, that they could break God's law and yet, as he assured her, "You positively will not die." (Genesis 3:4; James 1:13-15) His statements implied that they did not need their Creator in order for them to have continued life and happiness. In fact, he said that lawbreaking would actually improve matters for them, enabling them to be like God. Thus he called into question the validity of God's laws and cast doubt on God's way of governing them. Indeed, he cast doubt on their Creator's very *right* to rule. For this misrepresentation he came to be called *Satan,* which means "resister," and *Devil,* meaning "slanderer." For the past 6,000

9. How has all mankind been affected by the bad choice of the first humans?
10. (a) What rebellion took place in the spirit realm? (b) How could such a thing happen?

192

years this attitude of Satan has influenced mankind, advancing a policy of 'rule or ruin.'—Luke 4: 2-8; 1 John 5:19; Revelation 12:9.

[11] But why did God not destroy these lawbreakers, both human and spirit, at the start? The answer lies in the fact that profound issues had been raised before all intelligent creation. One of the issues involved questions such as: Would independence from God's sovereignty ever bring lasting benefits? Would God's direction of people be better for them, or would man's own direction be better? Could humans successfully govern this world independent of their Creator? In short, did humans really need God's guidance? These questions required answers that only the passing of time could supply.

Why So Long?

[12] However, why has God permitted so much time to go by before settling these matters—about 6,000 years now? Could they not have been settled satisfactorily long ago? Well, if God had intervened long ago, the charge could have been made that humans were not given enough time to develop a workable government and the necessary technology to bring peace and prosperity to all. So, in his wisdom, God knew that it would take time to settle the issues that had been raised. He allowed that time.

It would take time to settle thoroughly the issues that had been raised

[13] Throughout the centuries, all types of governments, all types of social systems and all types of economic systems have been tried. In addition, humans have had enough time to make many technological advances, including harnessing the atom and traveling to the moon. With what results? Has all of this brought about the kind of world that is a real blessing to the entire human family?

[14] Far from it. Nothing that men have tried has

---

11. Why did God not wipe out the rebels at the start?
12. Had God interfered at the beginning, what charge could have been brought against him?
13, 14. What are the results of independence from God?

After all these centuries, world conditions are more threatening than ever

"All creation keeps on groaning together and being in pain together until now"

brought true peace and happiness for all. Instead, after all this time, conditions are more unstable than ever. Crime, war, family breakdown, poverty and hunger ravage country after country. Mankind's very existence has been jeopardized. Nuclear missiles of awesome destructive power could annihilate most of, if not all, the human race. So, in spite of thousands of years of effort, in spite of many centuries of human experience to build upon and in spite of reaching new peaks of technological progress, mankind still grapples unsuccessfully with its most basic problems.

[15] Even the earth itself has been adversely affected. Human greed and neglect have turned certain areas into deserts by stripping protective forests. Chemicals and other waste products have polluted land, sea and air. The Bible's description, 2,000 years ago, of the condition of life on the earth is even more accurate today: "All creation keeps on groaning together and being in pain together until now."—Romans 8:22.

What Has Been Proved?

[16] What have events during all this time proved beyond a doubt? That human rule independent of

15. What has happened to the earth as a consequence of man's rebellion?
16, 17. What has been proved by the passing of so much time?

194

man's Creator is unsatisfactory. Clearly it has been demonstrated that successful management of earth's affairs is impossible apart from man's Maker. History continues to confirm the Bible's candid appraisal of human attempts to govern when it says: "Man has dominated man to his injury."—Ecclesiastes 8:9.

By allowing enough time to answer the questions, God has established a precedent for the future, like a fundamental supreme court decision

[17] How disastrously human endeavors have worked out, compared with the order and precision found in the universe as it is guided by the laws of its Creator! Clearly, humans also need this kind of guidance in governing their affairs, because ignoring God's supervision has been disastrous. It truly has been demonstrated, for all time, that we have a need for God's direction just as surely as we need air, water and food.—Matthew 4:4.

[18] Also, by allowing enough time to settle the issues relative to human rule, God has established a permanent precedent for the future. It could be likened to a fundamental supreme court case. For all time the issue has been settled: Human rule apart from God cannot bring about desirable conditions on the earth. Thus, in the future, if any free agent should challenge God's way of doing things, it would not be necessary to allow thousands of additional years to try to prove his contention.

18. How has allowing time to settle the questions provided a permanent precedent for the future?

195

Everything that needs to be proved has been proved in this period of about 6,000 years that God has allowed. So, throughout the eternity of time ahead, no rebel will ever again be allowed to mar the peace and happiness of life on the earth, or to interfere with God's sovereignty anywhere else in the universe. As the Bible emphatically states: "Distress will not rise up a second time."—Nahum 1:9.

God's Solution

[19] Thus the Bible provides a reasonable explanation for the existence of suffering in a world created by God. Also the Bible clearly shows that the time is near when God will use his almighty power to remove those who cause suffering. Proverbs 2: 21, 22 states: "The upright are the ones that will reside in the earth, and the blameless are the ones that will be left over in it. As regards the wicked, they will be cut off from the very earth; and as for the treacherous, they will be torn away from it." Yes, God will "bring to ruin those ruining the earth." (Revelation 11:18) That will also include, finally, the elimination of Satan the Devil. (Romans 16:20) God will not allow the wicked to mar his beautiful creation, the earth, much longer. Any who do not conform to his laws will be uprooted. Only those who do God's will are to continue living. (1 John 2:15-17) You would not plant a flower garden in a weed patch, nor place chickens and foxes in the same coop. So, too, when God restores Paradise for righteous humans, he will not let vandals run loose at the same time.

The Creator will not allow the wicked to mar his beautiful earth much longer

[20] While the suffering of centuries has been very painful for those who have been victimized by it, it has served a good purpose. It could be compared to permitting your child to have a painful operation to correct a major health problem. The long-term benefits far outweigh any temporary pain. In addition,

19. What is God's solution to the problem of wickedness?
20. How will the suffering of the past be erased?

196

the future that God has purposed for this earth and humans on it will lift the weight of the past from memory: "The former things will not be called to mind, neither will they come up into the heart." (Isaiah 65:17) Hence, whatever suffering that humans have experienced will eventually be erased from the minds of those living when God's rulership holds sway over all the earth. At that time the joys will crowd out all the previous bad memories, for God "'will wipe out every tear from their eyes, and death will be no more, neither will mourning nor outcry nor pain be anymore. The former things

Whatever suffering that people have previously experienced will be erased by the joys in God's New Order

have passed away.' And the One seated on the throne said: 'Look! I am making all things new.'" —Revelation 21:4, 5.

[21] Jesus Christ spoke of this coming New Order as "the re-creation." (Matthew 19:28) The past victims of suffering and death then will learn that God does care about them, because that era will also see the literal re-creating of those who are dead in the grave. Jesus said: "All those in the memorial tombs . . . will come out" in a resurrection to life on earth. (John 5:28, 29) In this way, the dead also will be given the opportunity to submit to God's righteous rule and gain the privilege of living forever "in Paradise," as Jesus called it.—Luke 23:43.

[22] Even the animal realm will be at peace. The Bible says that "the wolf and the lamb themselves will feed as one, and the lion will eat straw just like the bull," and even "a mere little boy will be leader over them." The animals will "do no harm nor cause any ruin" in God's New Order, to one another or to humans.—Isaiah 11:6-9; 65:25.

[23] Thus, in every way, as Romans 8:21 states, "the creation itself also will be set free from enslavement to corruption and have the glorious freedom of the children of God." In time, the earth will become a paradise, inhabited by perfect people —free from sickness, sorrow and death. Suffering will be forever a thing of the past. All aspects of God's earthly creation will come into complete harmony with his purpose, removing the ugly blot that has marred his universe for thousands of years.

[24] This is how the Bible explains God's permission of suffering, and what he will do to solve the problem. Yet, some may ask: 'How do I know that I can really trust what the Bible says?'

In every way "the creation itself also will be set free from enslavement to corruption"

---

21. What opportunity will be given even to dead people?
22. What condition will be restored to the animal realm?
23. Into what condition will all of God's creation come?
24. What question may be asked about the Bible?

198

Chapter 17

Can You Trust the Bible?

MANY view the Bible simply as a book written by wise men of a bygone era. A university professor, Gerald A. Larue, asserted: "The views of the writers as expressed in the Bible reflect the ideas, beliefs, and concepts current in their own times and are limited by the extent of knowledge in those times."[1] Yet the Bible claims to be a book inspired by God. (2 Timothy 3:16) If this is true, it would surely be free from mistaken views prevailing at the time its various parts were written. Can the Bible withstand examination in the light of present knowledge?

[2] As we consider this question keep in mind that, with the progress of knowledge, humans constantly must keep adjusting their views to conform to new information and discoveries. The *Scientific Monthly* once observed: "It is too much to expect that articles written in some cases as [recently] as five years ago could now be accepted as representative of the latest thinking in the areas of science with which they are concerned."[2] Yet the Bible was written and compiled during a period of some 1,600 years, and was completed nearly 2,000 years ago. What can be said today about its accuracy?

The Bible and Science

[3] When the Bible was being written, there was speculation regarding how the earth was held in

---

1. (a) What view do many have of the Bible, as opposed to the Bible's own claim? (b) What question arises?
2. How does new information often affect the writings of humans on scientific matters?
3. What views did ancient people have regarding the earth's support, but what does the Bible say?

This is how some ancients believed that the earth was supported

space. Some, for example, believed that the earth was supported by four elephants standing on a big sea turtle. Yet rather than reflect the fanciful, unscientific views existing at its time of writing, the Bible simply stated: "[God] is stretching out the north over the empty place, *hanging the earth upon nothing.*" (Job 26:7) Yes, over 3,000 years ago the Bible correctly noted that the earth has no visible support, a fact that is in harmony with the more recently understood laws of gravity and motion. "How Job knew the truth," observed one religious scholar, "is a question not easily solved by those who deny the inspiration of Holy Scripture."[3]

4 Regarding the shape of the earth, *The Encyclopedia Americana* says: "The earliest known image that men had of the earth was that it was a flat, rigid platform at the center of the universe. . . . The concept of a spherical earth was not widely accepted until the Renaissance."[4] Some early navigators even feared sailing off the edge of the flat earth! But, then, the introduction of the compass and other improvements made possible longer ocean voyages. These "voyages of discovery," another encyclopedia explains, "showed that the world was round, not flat as most people had believed."[5]

5 Yet long before such voyages, in fact, about

4, 5. (a) What did people once believe about the shape of the earth, causing what fear? (b) What does the Bible say regarding the shape of the earth?

200

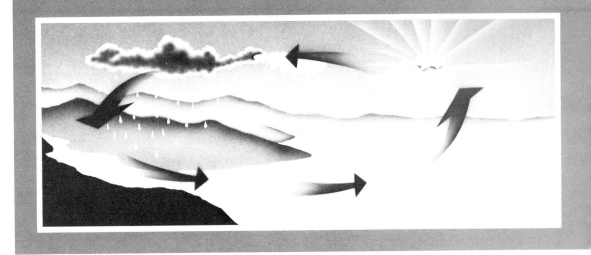

2,700 years ago, the Bible said: "There is One who is dwelling above the *circle* of the earth, the dwellers in which are as grasshoppers." (Isaiah 40:22) The Hebrew word *chugh,* translated "circle," can also mean "sphere," as such reference works as Davidson's *Analytical Hebrew and Chaldee Lexicon* show. Other translations, therefore, say "the *globe* of the earth" (*Douay Version*), and "the *round* earth." (*Moffatt*) Thus the Bible was not influenced by the erroneous, flat-earth view prevalent when it was written. It was accurate.

⁶ Humans have long noted that the rivers flow into the seas and oceans and yet these do not increase in depth. Some believed, until it was learned that the earth is spherical, that this was because an equal amount of water was spilling off the ends of the earth. Later it was learned that the sun "pumps" up thousands of millions of gallons of water from the seas every second in the form of water vapor. This produces clouds that are moved by the wind over land areas where the moisture falls as rain and snow. Water then runs into the rivers and flows again into the seas. This marvelous cycle, although generally unknown in ancient times, is spoken about in the Bible: "Every river flows into the sea, but the sea is not yet full. The water returns to where the rivers began, and starts

This water cycle, generally unknown in ancient times, is described in the Bible

---

6. What marvelous cycle, generally not understood in ancient times, does the Bible describe?

all over again."—Ecclesiastes 1:7, *Today's English Version*.

7 Regarding the origin of the universe, the Bible states: "In the beginning God created the heavens and the earth." (Genesis 1:1) But many scientists had considered this unscientific, asserting that the universe had no beginning. However, pointing to newer information, astronomer Robert Jastrow explains: "The essence of the strange developments is that the Universe had, in some sense, a beginning —that it began at a certain moment in time." Jastrow here refers to the now commonly accepted big bang theory, as noted in Chapter 9. He adds: "Now we see how the astronomical evidence leads to a biblical view of the origin of the world. The details differ, but the essential elements in the astronomical and biblical accounts of Genesis are the same."[6]

"The astronomical and biblical accounts of Genesis are the same"

8 What has been the reaction to such discoveries? "Astronomers are curiously upset," Jastrow writes. "Their reactions provide an interesting demonstration of the response of the scientific mind—supposedly a very objective mind—when evidence uncovered by science itself leads to a conflict with the articles of faith in our profession. It turns out that the scientist behaves the way the rest of us do when our beliefs are in conflict with the evidence. We become irritated, we pretend the conflict does not exist, or we paper it over with meaningless phrases."[7] But the fact remains that while "evidence uncovered by science" disagreed with what scientists long believed regarding the origin of the universe, it confirmed what was written in the Bible millenniums ago.

9 In the days of Noah, the Bible says, a great flood covered earth's highest mountains and de-

7, 8. (a) How has the Bible been proved accurate in what it says about the origin of the universe? (b) What is the reaction of some astronomers regarding this newer information, and why?
9, 10. (a) What does the Bible say about a great flood? (b) What evidence now verifies that what the Bible says is true?

stroyed all human life that was outside the huge ark that Noah built. (Genesis 7:1-24) Many have scoffed at this account. Yet seashells are found on high mountains. And further evidence that a flood of immense proportions occurred in the not-too-distant past is the great number of fossils and carcasses deposited in icy, mucky dumps. *The Saturday Evening Post* noted: "Many of these animals were perfectly fresh, whole and undamaged, and still either standing or at least kneeling upright. . . . Here is a really shocking—to our previous way of thinking—picture. Vast herds of enormous, well-fed beasts not specifically designed for extreme cold, placidly feeding in sunny pastures . . . Suddenly they were all killed without any visible sign of violence and before they could so much as swallow a last mouthful of food, and then were quick-frozen so rapidly that every cell of their bodies is perfectly preserved."[8]

Frozen-solid mammoth uncovered in Siberia. After thousands of years, vegetation was still in its mouth and stomach, and its flesh was edible when thawed out

[10] This fits in with what happened in the great Flood. The Bible describes it in these words: "All the springs of the vast watery deep were broken open and the floodgates of the heavens were opened." The downpour "overwhelmed the earth," being accompanied no doubt by freezing winds in the polar regions. (Genesis 1:6-8; 7:11, 19) There, the temperature change would be the most rapid and drastic. Various forms of life were thus engulfed and preserved in frozen muck. One such may have been the mammoth that was uncovered by excavators in Siberia and that is seen in the accompanying illustration. Vegetation was still in its mouth and stomach, and its flesh was even edible when thawed out.

[11] The closer the Bible is examined, the more astonishing is its remarkable accuracy. As noted on pages 36 and 37 of this book, the Bible gives the

---

11. What else in the Bible has been confirmed by increased knowledge, leading even some scientists to what conclusion?

203

stages of creation in the very order science now confirms, a fact hard to explain if the Bible were simply of human origin. This is another example of the many details in the Bible that have been confirmed by increasing knowledge. With good reason one of the greatest scientists of all time, Isaac Newton, said: "No sciences are better attested than the religion of the Bible."[9]

The Bible and Health

[12] Throughout the centuries there has been great ignorance on matters of health. A physician even observed: "Many superstitions are still believed by large numbers of people such as, that a buckeye in the pocket will prevent rheumatism; that handling toads will cause warts; that wearing red flannel around the neck will cure a sore throat," and others. Yet he explained: "No such statements are found in the Bible. This in itself is remarkable."[10]

The Bible is remarkably free from superstitious expressions

[13] It is also remarkable when one compares hazardous medical treatments used in the past with what the Bible says. For example, the Papyrus Ebers, a medical document of the ancient Egyptians, prescribed the use of excrement to treat various conditions. It directed that human excrement mixed with fresh milk be applied as a poultice to lesions that remain after scabs fall off. And a remedy for drawing out splinters reads: "Worms' blood, cook and crush in oil; mole, kill, cook, and drain in oil; ass's dung, mix in fresh milk. Apply to the opening."[11] Such treatment, it is now known, can result in serious infections.

[14] What does the Bible say about excrement? It directed: "When you squat outside, you must also

12. How did a physician contrast common superstitions regarding health with statements in the Bible?
13. What hazardous medical treatment was prescribed by ancient Egyptians?
14. What does the Bible say about waste disposal, and how has this been a protection?

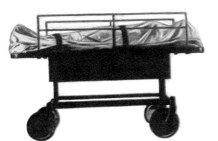

dig a hole with [a digging instrument] and turn and cover your excrement." (Deuteronomy 23:13) So, far from prescribing excrement in medical treatment, the Bible directed the safe disposal of sewage. Up until the present century the danger of leaving excrement exposed to flies was generally not known. This resulted in the spread of serious fly-borne diseases and the death of many people. Yet the simple remedy was on record in the Bible all the time, and it was followed by the Israelites over 3,000 years ago.

In the past century, doctors did not always wash after touching the dead, causing other deaths

15 During the last century medical personnel would go directly from handling the dead in the dissecting room to conducting examinations in the maternity ward, and they would not even wash their hands. Infection was thus transferred from the dead, and many others died. Even when the value of hand washing was demonstrated, many in the medical community resisted such hygienic measures. Doubtless unknown to them, they were rejecting the wisdom in the Bible, since Jehovah's law to the Israelites decreed that anyone touching a dead person became unclean and must wash himself and his garments.—Numbers 19:11-22.

16 As a sign of a covenant with Abraham, Jehovah God said: "Every male of yours *eight days old* must be circumcised." Later this requirement was repeated to the nation of Israel. (Genesis 17:12; Leviticus

---

15. If Bible advice regarding touching dead persons had been followed, what medical practice resulting in many deaths would have been avoided?
16. How was wisdom beyond human knowledge shown in directing that circumcision be performed on the eighth day?

12:2, 3) No explanation was given why the *eighth* day was specified, but now we understand. Medical research has discovered that the blood-clotting element vitamin K rises to an adequate level only by then. Another essential clotting element, prothrombin, seems to be higher on the eighth day than at any other time during a child's life. Based on this evidence, Dr. S. I. McMillen concluded: "The perfect day to perform a circumcision is the *eighth* day."[12] Was this mere coincidence? Not at all. It was knowledge passed on by a God who knew.

[17] Another discovery of modern science is the degree to which mental attitude and emotions affect health. An encyclopedia explains: "Since 1940 it has become more and more apparent that the physiologic function of organs and the organs systems are closely allied to the state of mind of the individual and that even tissue changes may occur in an organ so affected."[13] However, this close connection between mental attitude and physical health was long ago referred to in the Bible. For instance, it says: "A calm heart is the life of the fleshly organism, but jealousy is rottenness to the bones." —Proverbs 14:30; 17:22.

The close connection between mental attitude and physical health was long ago referred to in the Bible

[18] The Bible, therefore, directs people away from damaging emotions and attitudes. "Let us walk decently," it admonishes, "not in strife and jealousy." It also counsels: "Let all malicious bitterness and anger and wrath and screaming and abusive speech be taken away from you along with all badness. But become kind to one another, tenderly compassionate." (Romans 13:13; Ephesians 4:31, 32) Especially does the Bible recommend love. "Besides all these things," it says, "clothe yourselves with love." As the greatest proponent of love, Jesus told his disciples: "I am giving you a new commandment, that you love one another; just as I have loved

17. What is another discovery of science that confirms the Bible?
18. How does the Bible direct people away from damaging emotions and emphasize showing love?

you." In his Sermon on the Mount he even said: "Continue to love your enemies." (Colossians 3: 12-15; John 13:34; Matthew 5:44) Many may scoff at this, calling it weakness, but they pay a price. Science has learned that lack of love is a major factor in many mental ills and other problems.

[19] The British medical journal *Lancet* once noted: "By far the most significant discovery of mental science is the power of love to protect and to restore the mind."[14] Similarly, a noted stress specialist, Dr. Hans Selye, said: "It is not the hated person or the frustrating boss who will get ulcers, hypertensions, and heart disease. It is the one who hates or the one who permits himself to be frustrated. 'Love thy neighbor' is one of the sagest bits of medical advice ever given."[15]

[20] Indeed, the Bible's wisdom is far ahead of modern discoveries. As Dr. James T. Fisher once wrote: "If you were to take the sum total of all the authoritative articles ever written by the most qualified of psychologists and psychiatrists on the subject of mental hygiene—if you were to combine them, and refine them, and cleave out the excess verbiage—if you were to take the whole of the meat and none of the parsley, and if you were to have these unadulterated bits of pure scientific knowledge concisely expressed by the most capable of living poets, you would have an awkward and incomplete summation of the Sermon on the Mount."[16]

The Bible's emphasis on love harmonizes with sound medical advice

The Bible and History

[21] After Darwin's publication of his theory of evolution, the Bible's historical record came under widespread attack. Archaeologist Leonard Woolley explained: "There arose towards the close of the

---

19. What has modern science discovered regarding love?
20. How did a doctor compare Christ's teachings in the Sermon on the Mount with psychiatric advice?
21. About a hundred years ago, how did critics view the historical value of the Bible?

nineteenth century an extreme school of critics which was ready to deny the historical foundation of practically everything related in the earlier books of the Old Testament."[17] In fact, some critics even claimed that writing did not come into common usage until the time of Solomon or afterward; and, therefore, the early Bible narratives could not be relied upon since they were not put into writing until centuries after the events occurred. One of the exponents of this theory said in 1892: "The time, of which the pre-Mosaic narratives treat, is a sufficient proof of their legendary character. It was a time prior to all knowledge of writing."[18]

[22] In recent times, however, a great deal of archaeological evidence has accumulated to show that writing was common long before the time of Moses. "We must again emphasize," archaeologist William Foxwell Albright explained, "that alphabetic Hebrew writing was employed in Canaan and neighboring districts from the Patriarchal Age on, and that the rapidity with which forms of letters changed is clear evidence of common use."[19] And another leading historian and excavator observed: "That the question should ever have been raised whether Moses could have known how to write, appears to us now absurd."[20]

[23] Time and again the Bible's historical record has been substantiated by the uncovering of new information. The Assyrian king Sargon, for example, was for a long time known only from the Bible account at Isaiah 20:1. In fact, during the early part of the last century this Bible reference to him was discounted by critics as of no historical value. Then archaeological excavations produced the ruins of Sargon's magnificent palace at Khorsabad, including many inscriptions regarding his rule. As

---

22. What has been learned about the ability of early peoples to write?
23. What was discovered regarding King Sargon, resulting in what revision of views?

a result, Sargon is now one of the best known of the Assyrian kings. Israeli historian Moshe Pearlman wrote: "Suddenly, sceptics who had doubted the authenticity even of the historical parts of the Old Testament began to revise their views."[21]

[24] One of Sargon's inscriptions tells of an episode that previously had been known only from the Bible. It reads: "I besieged and conquered Samaria, led away as booty 27,290 inhabitants of it."[22] The Bible account of this at 2 Kings 17:6 reads: "In the ninth year of Hoshea, the king of Assyria captured Samaria and then led Israel into exile." Regarding the striking similarity of these two accounts, Pearlman observed: "Here, then, were two reports in the annals of the conqueror and the vanquished, one almost a mirror of the other."[23]

A limestone relief of King Sargon, who had long been known only from the Bible account

[25] Should we expect, then, that Biblical and secular records would agree in every detail? No, as Pearlman notes: "This kind of identical 'war reporting' from both sides was unusual in the Middle East of ancient times (and on occasion in modern times too). It occurred only when the countries in conflict were Israel and one of its neighbours, and only when Israel was defeated. *When Israel won, no record of failure appeared in the chronicles of the enemy."*[24] (Italics added.) It is not surprising, therefore, that Assyrian accounts of the military campaign into Israel by Sargon's son, Sennacherib, have a major omission. And what is that?

[26] Wall reliefs from King Sennacherib's palace have been discovered that depict scenes of his expedition into Israel. Written descriptions of it were also found. One, a clay prism, reads: "As to Hezekiah, the Jew, he did not submit to my yoke, I laid

---

24. How closely does an Assyrian account of Sargon compare with the Bible account regarding the conquest of Samaria?
25. Why should we not expect that Biblical and secular records would agree in every respect?
26. How does the account by Sennacherib compare with that found in the Bible regarding his military expedition into Israel?

A wall relief from King Sennacherib's palace in Nineveh, showing him receiving booty from the Judean city of Lachish

This clay prism of King Sennacherib describes his military expedition into Israel

siege to 46 of his strong cities . . . Himself I made a prisoner in Jerusalem, his royal residence, like a bird in a cage. . . . I reduced his country, but I still increased the tribute and the *katrû*-presents (due) to me (as his) overlord."[25] So, Sennacherib's version coincides with the Bible where Assyrian victories are concerned. But, as expected, he omits mentioning his failure to conquer Jerusalem and the fact that he was forced to return home because 185,000 of his soldiers had been killed in one night. —2 Kings 18:13–19:36; Isaiah 36:1–37:37.

[27] Consider Sennacherib's assassination and what a recent discovery reveals. The Bible says that *two* of his sons, Adrammelech and Sharezer, put Sennacherib to death. (2 Kings 19:36, 37) Yet both the account attributed to Babylonian King Nabonidus and that of the Babylonian priest Berossus of the third century B.C.E. mention only *one* son as involved in the slaying. Which was correct? Commenting on the more recent discovery of a fragmentary prism of Esar-haddon, Sennacherib's son who succeeded him as king, historian Philip Biberfeld wrote: "Only the Biblical account proved to be correct. It was confirmed in all the minor details by the inscription of Esar-haddon and proved to be more accurate regarding this event of Babylonian-Assyrian history than the Babylonian sources themselves. This is a fact of utmost importance for the evaluation of even contemporary sources not in accord with Biblical tradition."[26]

[28] At one time all known ancient sources also

---

27. How does the Bible's account of Sennacherib's assassination compare with what ancient secular accounts say about it?
28. How has the Bible been vindicated in what it says about Belshazzar?

differed with the Bible regarding Belshazzar. The Bible presents Belshazzar as the king of Babylon when it fell. (Daniel 5:1-31) However, secular writings did not even mention Belshazzar, saying that Nabonidus was king at the time. So critics claimed that Belshazzar never existed. More recently, however, ancient writings were found that identified Belshazzar as a son of Nabonidus and coruler with his father in Babylon. For this reason, evidently, the Bible says Belshazzar offered to make Daniel "the third ruler in the kingdom," since Belshazzar himself was the second. (Daniel 5:16, 29) Thus the Yale University professor, R. P. Dougherty, when comparing the Bible book of Daniel with other ancient writings, said: "The Scriptural account may be interpreted as excelling because it employs the name Belshazzar, because it attributes royal power to Belshazzar, and because it recognizes that a dual rulership existed in the kingdom."[27]

Victory monument of Esar-haddon, son of Sennacherib, amplifies 2 Kings 19:37: "And Esar-haddon his son began to reign in place of him"

[29] Another example of a discovery that confirms the historicalness of a person mentioned in the Bible is given by Michael J. Howard, who worked with the Caesarea expedition in Israel in 1979. "For 1,900 years," he wrote, "Pilate existed only on the pages of the Gospels and in the vague recollections of Roman and Jewish historians. Next to nothing was known about his life. Some said he never even existed. But in 1961, an Italian archaeological expedition was working in the ruins of the ancient Roman theater in Caesarea. A workman overturned a stone that had been used for one of the stairways. On the reverse side was the following, partially-obscured inscription in Latin: 'Caesariensibus Tiberium Pontius Pilatus Praefectus Iudaeae.' (To the people of Caesarea Tiberium Pontius Pilate Prefect of Judea.) It was a fatal blow to the doubts about Pilate's existence. . . . For the first time there was contemporary epigraphic evidence of the life of the

This inscription, found in Caesarea, verifies that Pontius Pilate was governor of Judea

---

29. What confirmation has been discovered regarding what the Bible says about Pontius Pilate?

This wall relief verifies the record found in the Bible of Shishak's victory over Judah

The Moabite Stone records the revolt of Moab's King Mesha against Israel, described in the Bible

man who ordered the crucifixion of Christ."[28]—John 19:13-16; Acts 4:27.

[30] Modern discoveries even substantiate minor details of ancient Bible accounts. For instance, contradicting the Bible, Werner Keller wrote in 1964 that camels were not domesticated at an early date, and, therefore, the scene where "we meet Rebecca for the first time in her native city of Nahor must make do with a change of stage props. The 'camels' belonging to her future father-in-law, Abraham, which she watered at the well were—donkeys."[29] (Genesis 24:10) However, in 1978 Israeli military leader and archaeologist Moshe Dayan pointed to evidence that camels "served as a means of transport" in those early times, and hence that the Bible account is accurate. "An eighteenth-century BC relief found at Byblos in Phoenicia depicts a kneeling camel," Dayan explained. "And camel riders appear on cylinder seals recently discovered in Mesopotamia belonging to the patriarchal period."[30]

[31] Evidence that the Bible is historically accurate has mounted irresistibly. While it is true that secular records of Egypt's Red Sea debacle and other such defeats have not been found, this is not surprising since it was not the practice of rulers to record their defeats. Yet, discovered on the temple walls of Karnak in Egypt is the record of Pharaoh Shishak's successful invasion of Judah during the reign of Solomon's son Rehoboam. The Bible tells about this at 1 Kings 14:25, 26. In addition, Moabite

30. What has been discovered regarding the use of camels that substantiates the Bible record?
31. What further evidence is there that the Bible is historically accurate?

212

King Mesha's version of his revolt against Israel has been discovered, being recorded on what is called the Moabite Stone. The account can also be read in the Bible at 2 Kings 3:4-27.

King Jehu, or an emissary, paying tribute to King Shalmaneser III

[32] Visitors to many museums can see wall reliefs, inscriptions and statues that verify Bible accounts. Kings of Judah and Israel such as Hezekiah, Manasseh, Omri, Ahab, Pekah, Menahem and Hoshea appear on cuneiform records of Assyrian rulers. King Jehu or one of his emissaries is depicted on the Black Obelisk of Shalmaneser as paying tribute. The decor of the Persian palace of Shushan, as the Biblical characters Mordecai and Esther knew it, has been re-created for observation today. Statues of the early Roman Caesars, Augustus, Tiberius and Claudius, who appear in Bible accounts, can also be viewed by museum visitors. (Luke 2:1; 3:1; Acts 11:28; 18:2) A silver denarius coin, in fact, has been found that bears the image of Tiberius Caesar—a coin Jesus asked for when discussing the matter of taxes.—Matthew 22:19-21.

Marble bust of Augustus, the Caesar when Jesus Christ was born

[33] A modern-day visitor to Israel familiar with the Bible cannot help but be impressed with the fact that the Bible describes the land and its features with great accuracy. Dr. Ze'ev Shremer, leader of a geological expedition in the Sinai Peninsula, once said: "We have our own maps and geodetic survey plans, of course, but where the Bible and the maps are at odds, we opt for The Book."[31] To give an example of how one can personally experience the history presented in the Bible: In Jerusalem today a person can walk through a 1,749-foot-long tunnel that was cut through solid rock over 2,700 years ago. It was cut to protect the city's water supply by carrying water from the hidden spring of Gihon outside the city walls to the Pool of Siloam within

A silver denarius with Tiberius Caesar's inscription, like the one Christ asked for

---

32. What can visitors to museums today see that verifies Bible accounts?
33. How does the land of Israel and its features provide evidence that the Bible is accurate?

Interior of tunnel that King Hezekiah had hewed out to provide water for Jerusalem during Assyrian siege

the city. The Bible explains how Hezekiah had this water tunnel constructed to provide water for the city in anticipation of Sennacherib's coming siege. —2 Kings 20:20; 2 Chronicles 32:30.

[34] These are but a few examples that illustrate why it is unwise to underestimate the Bible's accuracy. There are many, many more. So doubts about the Bible's reliability are usually based, not on what it says or upon sound evidence, but instead upon misinformation or ignorance. The former director of the British Museum, Frederic Kenyon, wrote: "Archæology has not yet said its last word; but the results already achieved confirm what faith would suggest, that the Bible can do nothing but gain from an increase of knowledge."[32] And the well-known archaeologist Nelson Glueck said: "It may be stated categorically that no archaeological discovery has ever controverted a Biblical reference. Scores of archaeological findings have been made which confirm in clear outline or in exact detail historical statements in the Bible."[33]

Honesty and Harmony

[35] Something else that identifies the Bible as coming from God is the honesty of its writers. It is contrary to imperfect human nature to admit mistakes or failures, especially in writing. Most ancient writers reported only their successes and virtues. Yet Moses wrote how he had "acted undutifully," and so was disqualified from leading Israel into the Promised Land. (Deuteronomy 32:50-52; Numbers 20:1-13) Jonah told of his own waywardness. (Jonah 1:1-3; 4:1) Paul acknowledges his former wrongdoings. (Acts 22:19, 20; Titus 3:3) And Matthew, an apostle of Christ, reported that the

---

34. What have some respected scholars said about the Bible's accuracy?
35, 36. (a) What personal shortcomings did various Bible writers acknowledge? (b) Why does the honesty of these writers add weight to their claim that the Bible is from God?

apostles at times showed little faith, sought prominence and even abandoned Jesus at his arrest. —Matthew 17:18-20; 18:1-6; 20:20-28; 26:56.

[36] If Bible writers were going to falsify anything, would it not be unfavorable information about themselves? They would not likely reveal their own shortcomings and then make false claims about other things, would they? So, then, the honesty of the Bible writers adds weight to their claim that God guided them as they wrote.—2 Timothy 3:16.

It is contrary to human nature to admit mistakes or failures, especially in writing

[37] The internal harmony around a central theme also testifies to the Bible's Divine Authorship. It is easy to state that the Bible's 66 books were written over a period of 16 centuries by some 40 different writers. But think how remarkable that fact is! Say that the writing of a book began during the time of the Roman Empire, that the writing continued through the period of the monarchies and to modern-day republics, and that the writers were people as different as soldiers, kings, priests, fishermen, and even a herdsman as well as a medical doctor. Would you expect every part of that book to follow the same precise theme? Yet the Bible was written over a similar period of time, under various political regimes, and by men of all those categories. And it is harmonious throughout. Its basic message has the same thrust from beginning to end. Does this not lend weight to the Bible's claim that these "men spoke from God as they were borne along by holy spirit"?—2 Peter 1:20, 21.

The Bible is harmonious throughout

[38] Can you trust the Bible? If you really examine what it says, and do not simply accept what certain ones claim that it says, you will find reason to trust it. Yet, even stronger evidence exists that the Bible was indeed inspired by God, which is the subject of the next chapter.

---

37. Why is the internal harmony of the Bible such strong evidence that it is inspired by God?
38. What does it take for a person to trust the Bible?

Chapter 18

The Bible—Is It Really Inspired by God?

NO MAN can accurately foretell the future in detail. That is beyond human ability. However, the Creator of the universe possesses all the necessary facts and can even control events. Thus he can be spoken of as the One who is "telling from the beginning the finale, and from long ago the things that have not been done."—Isaiah 46:10; 41:22, 23.

[2] The Bible contains hundreds of prophecies. Have they been accurately fulfilled until now? If so, it would be a telling indication of the Bible's being "inspired of God." (2 Timothy 3:16, 17) And it would create confidence in further prophecies regarding events yet to come. Hence, it will be useful to review some prophecies already fulfilled.

Fulfilled prophecies create confidence

The Fall of Tyre

[3] Tyre was a prominent seaport of Phoenicia that had dealt treacherously with ancient Israel, her southern neighbor that worshiped Jehovah. Through a prophet named Ezekiel, Jehovah foretold its complete destruction over 250 years before it happened. Jehovah declared: "I will bring up against you many nations . . . And they will certainly bring the walls of Tyre to ruin and tear down her towers, and I will scrape her dust away from her and make her a shining, bare surface of a crag. A drying yard for dragnets is what she will become in the midst of the sea." Ezekiel also named in advance the first nation and its leader to besiege

---

1. What ability does the Creator possess that humans do not?
2. What telling evidence would indicate that the Bible is inspired by God?
3. What was foretold concerning Tyre?

Tyre: "Here I am bringing against Tyre Nebuchadrezzar the king of Babylon."—Ezekiel 26:3-5, 7.

[4] As foretold, Nebuchadrezzar [Nebuchadnezzar] did later overthrow mainland Tyre, *The Encyclopœdia Britannica* reporting "a 13-year siege . . . by Nebuchadrezzar."[1] After the siege it was reported that he took no spoils: "As for wages, there proved to be none for him." (Ezekiel 29:18) Why not? Because part of Tyre was on an island across a narrow channel.[2] Most of Tyre's treasures had been transferred from the mainland to that island part of the city, which was not defeated.

[5] But Nebuchadrezzar's conquest did not "scrape [Tyre's] dust away from her and make her a shining, bare surface" as Ezekiel had foretold. Nor was Zechariah's prophecy fulfilled, which said that Tyre would be pitched "into the sea." (Zechariah 9:4) Were these prophecies inaccurate? Not at all. Over 250 years after Ezekiel's prophecy and nearly 200 years after Zechariah's, Tyre was totally destroyed by Greek armies under Alexander the Great, in 332 B.C.E. "With the debris of the mainland portion of the city," explains the *Encyclopedia*

Building the causeway to reach the island city of Tyre fulfilled Bible prophecy

---

4. (a) How was the prophecy regarding Babylon's conquest of Tyre fulfilled? (b) Why did the Babylonians fail to take spoils?
5, 6. How did Alexander the Great destroy the island city of Tyre and fulfill in detail what had been prophesied?

217

Bible prophecy was fulfilled by the draining of the Euphrates River

Americana, "he built a huge [causeway] in 332 to join the island to the mainland. After a seven months' siege . . . he captured and destroyed Tyre."[3]

6 Thus, as predicted by Ezekiel and Zechariah, Tyre's dust and debris did end up in the midst of the water. She was left a bare crag, "a place to spread nets upon," as a visitor to the site observed.[4] So, prophecies spoken hundreds of years earlier were fulfilled in exact detail!

Cyrus and the Fall of Babylon

7 Also remarkable are the prophecies involving the Jews and Babylon. History records that Babylon took the Jews into captivity. Yet, about 40 years before this happened Jeremiah foretold it. Isaiah predicted it some 150 years before it happened. He also foretold that the Jews would return from captivity. So did Jeremiah, saying that they would be restored to their land after 70 years. —Isaiah 39:6, 7; 44:26; Jeremiah 25:8-12; 29:10.

8 This return was made possible by the overthrow of Babylon by the Medes and Persians in 539 B.C.E.

7. What did the Bible foretell about the Jews and Babylon?
8, 9. (a) Who conquered Babylon, and how? (b) How does history verify the prophecy about Babylon?

It was foretold by Isaiah nearly 200 years before it happened, and by Jeremiah about 50 years before it occurred. Jeremiah said that the Babylonian soldiers would put up no fight. Both Isaiah and Jeremiah foretold that Babylon's protecting waters, the river Euphrates, "must be dried up." Isaiah even gave the name of the conquering Persian general, Cyrus, and said that before him "the gates [of Babylon] will not be shut."—Jeremiah 50:38; 51: 11, 30; Isaiah 13:17-19; 44:27; 45:1.

This clay Cyrus Cylinder (shown vertically) tells of Cyrus' practice of returning captives

⁹ The Greek historian Herodotus explained that Cyrus actually diverted the flow of the Euphrates and "the river sank to such an extent that the natural bed of the stream became fordable."⁵ Thus, during the night, enemy soldiers marched along the riverbed and entered the city through gates that had been carelessly left open. "Had the Babylonians been apprised of what Cyrus was about," Herodotus continued, "they would have made fast all the street-gates which [were] upon the river . . . But, as it was, the Persians came upon them by surprise and so took the city."⁶ Actually, the Babylonians were involved in drunken revelry, as the Bible explains, and as Herodotus confirms.⁷ (Daniel 5: 1-4, 30) Both Isaiah and Jeremiah foretold that Babylon would eventually become uninhabited ruins. And that is what happened. Today Babylon is a desolate heap of mounds.—Isaiah 13:20-22; Jeremiah 51:37, 41-43.

¹⁰ Cyrus also restored the Jews to their homeland. Over two centuries before, Jehovah had foretold of Cyrus: "All that I delight in he will completely carry out." (Isaiah 44:28) True to prophecy, after 70 years Cyrus returned the captives to their homeland, in 537 B.C.E. (Ezra 1:1-4) An ancient Persian inscription, called the Cyrus Cylinder, has been found that clearly states the policy of Cyrus to return captives to their homelands. "As to the inhabitants of Babylon," Cyrus is recorded as having

---

10. What evidence confirms the release of the Jews by Cyrus?

219

said, "I (also) gathered all their (former) inhabitants and returned (to them) their habitations."[8]

Medo–Persia and Greece

[11] While Babylon was still a world power the Bible foretold its conquest by a symbolic two-horned ram, representing "the kings of Media and Persia." (Daniel 8:20) As foretold, Medo-Persia became the next world power when it conquered Babylon in 539 B.C.E. In time, however, "a male of the goats," identified as Greece, "proceeded to strike down the ram and to break its two horns." (Daniel 8:1-7) This was in 332 B.C.E. when Greece defeated Medo-Persia and became the new world power.

Gold medallion depicting Alexander the Great, whose exploits were foretold in prophecy

[12] Note what was foretold to follow: "And the male of the goats, for its part, put on great airs to an extreme; but as soon as it became mighty, the great horn was broken, and there proceeded to come up conspicuously four instead of it." (Daniel 8:8) What does this mean? The Bible explains: "The hairy he-goat stands for the king of Greece; and as for the great horn that was between its eyes, it stands for the first king. And that one having been broken, so that there were four that finally stood up instead of it, there are four kingdoms from his nation that will stand up, but not with his power."—Daniel 8:21, 22.

[13] History shows that this "king of Greece" was Alexander the Great. But after his death in 323 B.C.E., his empire was eventually split up among four generals—Seleucus Nicator, Cassander, Ptolemy Lagus and Lysimachus. Just as the Bible had foretold, "there were four that finally stood up instead." Yet, as also foretold, none of these ever had the power that Alexander had. Thus, more than 200 years after this prophecy was re-

11. How did the Bible foretell Medo-Persia's rise to power and its fall to Greece?
12. What did the Bible say about the rulership of Greece?
13. Over 200 years after it was recorded, how was the prophecy about Greece fulfilled?

220

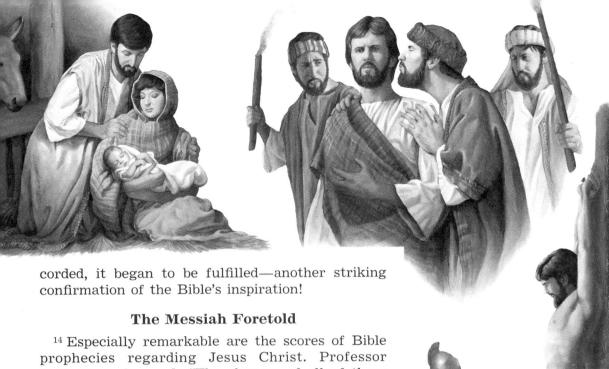

corded, it began to be fulfilled—another striking confirmation of the Bible's inspiration!

The Messiah Foretold

[14] Especially remarkable are the scores of Bible prophecies regarding Jesus Christ. Professor J. P. Free observed: "The chances of all of these prophecies being fulfilled in one man are so overwhelmingly remote that it is strikingly demonstrated that they could in no wise be the shrewd guesses of mere men."[9]

[15] The fulfilling of many of these prophecies was completely beyond the control of Jesus. He could not, for instance, have arranged to be born of the tribe of Judah, or as a descendant of David. (Genesis 49:10; Isaiah 9:6, 7; 11:1, 10; Matthew 1:2-16) Nor could he have maneuvered the events that led to his being born in Bethlehem. (Micah 5:2; Luke 2:1-7) Nor would he have arranged to be betrayed for 30 pieces of silver (Zechariah 11:12; Matthew 26:15); that his enemies spit on him (Isaiah 50:6; Matthew 26:67); that he be reviled while hanging from the executional stake (Psalm 22:7, 8; Matthew 27:39-43); that he be pierced, but not a bone in his body be broken (Zechariah 12:10; Psalm 34:20; John 19:33-37); and that soldiers cast lots for his garments (Psalm 22:18; Matthew 27:35).

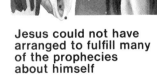

Jesus could not have arranged to fulfill many of the prophecies about himself

14. What did one scholar say about the many prophecies fulfilled by Jesus Christ?
15. What are some prophecies fulfilled in Christ that were beyond his control?

These are merely a few of the many prophecies fulfilled in the man Jesus.

The Destruction of Jerusalem

[16] Jesus was Jehovah's greatest Prophet. First, note what he said would happen to Jerusalem: "Your enemies will build around you a fortification with pointed stakes and will encircle you and distress you from every side, and they will dash you and your children within you to the ground, and they will not leave a stone upon a stone in you, because you did not discern the time of your being inspected." (Luke 19:43, 44) Jesus also said: "When you see Jerusalem surrounded by encamped armies, then know that the desolating of her has drawn near. Then let those in Judea begin fleeing to the mountains."—Luke 21:20, 21.

[17] True to the prophecy, Roman armies under Cestius Gallus came against Jerusalem in 66 C.E. Strangely, however, he did not press the siege to its completion, but, as the first-century historian Flavius Josephus reported: "He retired from the city, without any reason in the world."[10] With the siege unexpectedly lifted, opportunity was afforded to heed Jesus' instruction to flee Jerusalem. The historian Eusebius reported that it was the Christians who fled.[11]

The destruction of Jerusalem was foretold by Jesus

[18] Less than four years later, in 70 C.E., Roman armies under General Titus returned and encircled Jerusalem. They cut down trees for miles around and built a city-encircling wall, "a fortification with pointed stakes." As a result, Josephus observed: "All hope of escaping was now cut off from the Jews."[12] Josephus noted that after a siege of about five months, aside from three towers and a portion

16. What did Jesus prophesy regarding Jerusalem?
17. How was Jesus' prophecy about armies surrounding Jerusalem fulfilled, and so how could people flee the city?
18. (a) What happened in 70 C.E., less than four years after Roman armies had withdrawn from Jerusalem? (b) How complete was Jerusalem's destruction?

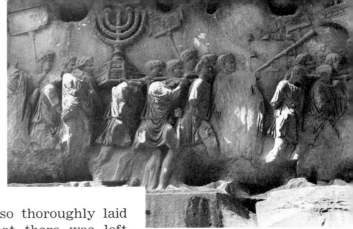

This wall relief inside the Arch of Titus, depicting treasures being carried off after Jerusalem's destruction, is a silent reminder

of a wall, what was left "was so thoroughly laid even with the ground . . . that there was left nothing to make those that came thither believe it had ever been inhabited."[13]

[19] About 1,100,000 died during the siege, and 97,000 were taken captive.[14] To this day a testimony to the fulfillment of Jesus' prophecy can be seen in Rome. There the Arch of Titus stands, erected by the Romans in 81 C.E. to commemorate the successful capture of Jerusalem. That arch remains a silent reminder to the fact that failure to heed the warnings in Bible prophecy can lead to disaster.

Prophecies Now Being Fulfilled

[20] According to the Bible, an astonishing world change is near. Just as Jesus foretold events by which people in the first century could know of the imminent destruction of Jerusalem, so he also foretold events by which people today could know that a world change is near. Jesus gave this "sign" in answer to this question by his disciples: "What will be the sign of your *presence* and of the *conclusion of the system of things?*"—Matthew 24:3.

[21] According to the Bible, this "presence" of Christ would not be in human form, but, rather, he would be a mighty ruler in heaven who will deliver oppressed humankind. (Daniel 7:13, 14) His "presence" would be during what he called "the conclu-

---

19. (a) How severe was the distress that came upon Jerusalem? (b) Of what is the Arch of Titus now a silent reminder?
20. In answer to what question did Jesus give the "sign" by which we could know that a great world change was near?
21. (a) What is Christ's "presence," and what is "the conclusion of the system of things"? (b) Where can we read about the sign that Jesus gave?

223

sion of the system of things." Well, then, just what was the sign that Jesus gave to mark the time when he would be invisibly present as ruler and when the end of this system of things would be near? In the Bible, at Matthew chapter 24, Mark chapter 13 and Luke chapter 21, you can review the events that together make up the sign. Some of the major ones are as follows:

[22] GREAT WARS: *"Nation will rise against nation and kingdom against kingdom."* (Matthew 24:7) From 1914 onward the fulfillment of this has been overwhelming. World War I, beginning in 1914, introduced the mass use of machine guns, tanks, submarines, airplanes, and also poison gas. By its end in 1918, about 14 million soldiers and civilians had been slaughtered. One historian noted: "The First World War was the first 'total' war."[15] World War II from 1939 to 1945 was even more destructive, with military and civilian deaths rising to some 55 million. And it introduced a totally new horror—atom bombs! Since then over 30 million more have been killed in scores of wars, large and small. The German newsmagazine *Der Spiegel* notes: "Not for a single day since 1945 has there been any real peace in the world."[16]

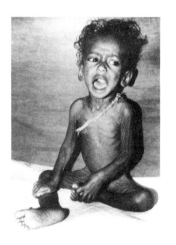

[23] FOOD SHORTAGES: *"There will be food shortages."* (Matthew 24:7) World War I was followed by widespread famine. After World War II famine was worse. And today? "Hunger today is on a totally new scale. . . . as many as 400 million live constantly on the brink of starvation," says the London *Times*.[17] *The Globe and Mail* of Toronto states: "More than 800 million people are underfed."[18] And the World Health Organization reports that "12 million children die each year before their first birthday" from the results of malnutrition.[19]

---

22. How have wars from 1914 onward been part of the sign, and how destructive were they?
23. To what extent have food shortages afflicted the world since 1914?

²⁴ EARTHQUAKES: *"There will be great earthquakes."* (Luke 21:11) A specialist in earthquake-proof engineering, George W. Housner, called the T'ang-shan, China, earthquake of 1976 "the greatest earthquake disaster in the history of mankind," taking hundreds of thousands of lives.[20] The Italian journal *Il Piccolo* reported: "Our generation lives in a dangerous period of high seismic activity, as statistics show."[21] On the average, about ten times as many have died each year from earthquakes since 1914 as in previous centuries.

²⁵ DISEASE: *"In one place after another pestilences."* (Luke 21:11) *Science Digest* reported: "The Spanish-influenza epidemic of 1918 sped over the earth [and] took 21 million lives." It added: "In all history there had been no sterner, swifter visitation of death. . . . had the epidemic continued its rate of acceleration, humanity would have been eradicated in a matter of months."[22] Since then, heart disease, cancer, venereal disease and many other plagues have maimed and killed hundreds of millions.

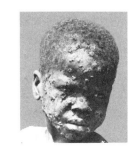

²⁶ CRIME: *"Increasing of lawlessness."* (Matthew 24:12) Murder, robbery, rape, terrorism, corruption —the list is long and well known. In many areas people fear to walk their streets. Confirming this lawless trend after 1914, an authority on terrorism states: "The period up to the first World War was, on the whole, more humane."[23]

²⁷ FEAR: *"Men become faint out of fear and expectation of the things coming upon the inhabited earth."* (Luke 21:26) Hamburg's *Die Welt* called our time "the century of fear."[24] Entirely new threats to mankind strike fear as never before. For the first time in history, such things as nuclear

24. What increase in earthquakes has there been since 1914?
25. What calamitous epidemics have there been since 1914 to fulfill part of the sign?
26. How has lawlessness increased since 1914?
27. The prophecy about fear is undergoing what fulfillment today?

225

annihilation and pollution threaten to 'ruin the earth.' (Revelation 11:18) Escalating crime, inflation, nuclear weapons, hunger, disease and other evils have fed the fear that people have concerning their security and their very lives.

What Makes It Different?

28 Yet, some point out that many of these things have happened in past centuries. So what makes their occurrence now any different? First, *every event* making up the sign has been *observed by one generation*—the generation that was living in 1914 —of which millions still survive. Jesus declared that "this generation will by no means pass away until all things occur." (Luke 21:32) Second, the effects of the sign are being *felt worldwide*, "in one place after another." (Matthew 24:3, 7, 9; 25:32) Third, conditions have *grown progressively worse* during this period: "All these things are a beginning of pangs of distress"; "wicked men and impostors will advance from bad to worse." (Matthew 24:8; 2 Timothy 3:13) And fourth, all these things have been accompanied by the *change in people's attitudes and actions* as Jesus warned: "The love of the greater number will cool off."—Matthew 24:12.

Every event making up the sign is being observed by one generation

29 Yes, one of the strong evidences that we are now living in the foretold crucial time of the end is seen in the moral breakdown among people. Compare what you observe in the world with these prophetic words regarding our time: "You must face the fact: the final age of this world is to be a time of troubles. Men will love nothing but money and self; they will be arrogant, boastful, and abusive; with no respect for parents, no gratitude, no piety, no natural affection; they will be implacable in their hatreds, scandal-mongers, intemperate and fierce, strangers to all goodness, traitors, adventur-

28. Why do the features of the sign occurring now identify our time as "the conclusion of the system of things"?
29. How does the Bible's description of "the final age of this world" match the moral condition of people today?

ers, swollen with self-importance. They will be men who put pleasure in the place of God, men who preserve the outward form of religion, but are a standing denial of its reality."—2 Timothy 3:1-5, *The New English Bible*.

1914—The Turning Point in History

[30] From the human standpoint, the world troubles and global wars foretold in the Bible were far from the thinking of the pre-1914 world. German statesman Konrad Adenauer said: "Thoughts and pictures come to my mind, . . . thoughts from the years before 1914 when there was real peace, quiet and security on this earth—a time when we didn't know fear. . . . Security and quiet have disappeared from the lives of men since 1914."[25] People living before 1914 thought that the future "would get better and better," reported British statesman Harold Macmillan.[26] The book *1913: America Between Two Worlds* notes: "Secretary of State Bryan said [in 1913] that 'conditions promising world peace were never more favorable than now.'"[27]

[31] So, right up to the very brink of World War I, world leaders were forecasting an age of social progress and enlightenment. But the Bible had foretold the opposite—that the unprecedented war of 1914 to 1918 would highlight the beginning of "the last days." (2 Timothy 3:1) The Bible also provided chronological evidence that 1914 would mark the birth of God's heavenly Kingdom, to be followed by unprecedented world trouble.[28] But was anyone living back then aware that 1914 would be such a turning point in history?

[32] Decades before that date, there was an organi-

"Before 1914 . . . there was real peace, quiet and security on this earth"

30, 31. (a) How did those living before 1914 view world conditions, and what did they think the future held? (b) In addition to the sign, what else does the Bible provide to show that we are in "the last days"?
32. (a) What were those who were familiar with Bible chronology saying about 1914 for decades before that date? (b) According to the accompanying chart, what have others said about 1914?

1914

A TURNING POINT IN HISTORY

Even after a second world war, many refer back to 1914 as the great turning point in modern history:

"It is indeed the year 1914 rather than that of Hiroshima which marks the turning point in our time."—René Albrecht-Carrié, *The Scientific Monthly*, July 1951.

"Ever since 1914, everybody conscious of trends in the world has been deeply troubled by what has seemed like a fated and predetermined march toward ever greater disaster. Many serious people have come to feel that nothing can be done to avert the plunge towards ruin. They see the human race, like the hero of a Greek tragedy, driven on by angry gods and no longer the master of fate."—Bertrand Russell, *The New York Times Magazine*, September 27, 1953.

"The modern era . . . began in 1914, and no one knows when or how it will end. . . . It could end in mass annihilation."—*The Seattle Times*, January 1, 1959.

"In the year 1914 the world, as it was known and accepted then, came to an end."—James Cameron, *1914*, published in 1959.

"The whole world really blew up about World War I and we still don't know why. . . . Utopia was in sight. There was peace and prosperity. Then everything blew up. We've been in a state of suspended animation ever since."—Dr. Walker Percy, *American Medical News*, November 21, 1977.

"In 1914 the world lost a coherence which it has not managed to recapture since. . . . This has been a time of extraordinary disorder and violence, both across national frontiers and within them."—*The Economist*, London, August 4, 1979.

"Civilization entered on a cruel and perhaps terminal illness in 1914."—Frank Peters, *St. Louis Post-Dispatch*, January 27, 1980.

"Everything would get better and better. This was the world I was born in. . . . Suddenly, unexpectedly, one morning in 1914 the whole thing came to an end."—British statesman Harold Macmillan, *The New York Times*, November 23, 1980.

zation of people who were making known the significance of 1914. The New York *World* of August 30, 1914, explains: "The terrific war outbreak in Europe has fulfilled an extraordinary prophecy. For a quarter of a century past, through preachers and through press, the 'International Bible Students' [Jehovah's Witnesses] . . . have been proclaiming to the world that the Day of Wrath prophesied in the Bible would dawn in 1914. 'Look out for 1914!' has been the cry of the . . . evangelists."[29]

A People Who Fulfill Prophecy

[33] The Bible also foretold that "in the final part of the days" people from all nations would be going, figuratively, "to the mountain of Jehovah" where he would "instruct [them] about his ways." The prophecy says that, as one result of such instruction, "they will have to beat their swords into plowshares and their spears into pruning shears. . . . *neither will they learn war anymore.*" (Isaiah 2:2-4) The well-known record of Jehovah's Witnesses regarding war is a clear fulfillment of this prophecy.

"Neither will they learn war anymore"

[34] Martin Niemöller, a Protestant leader in Germany before and after World War II, referred to Jehovah's Witnesses as "serious scholars of the Bible, who by the hundreds and thousands have gone into concentration camps and died because they refused to serve in war and declined to fire on human beings." By contrast, he wrote: "Christian Churches, throughout the ages, have always consented to bless war, troops and arms and . . . they prayed in a very un-Christian way for the annihilation of their enemy."[30] Who, then, measure up to the identifying mark that Jesus gave concerning true Christians? He said: "By this all will know that you are my disciples, if you have *love among yourselves.*" (John 13:35) As 1 John 3:10-12 makes

---

33. What additional part of the sign are Jehovah's Witnesses fulfilling?
34. What evidence is there that Jehovah's Witnesses have 'beaten their swords into plowshares'?

When this system ends, survivors will enter a new system of righteousness

clear, God's servants do not kill one another. It is Satan's children who do.

[35] A common allegiance to the Kingdom of God and faithful adherence to Bible principles is what unifies Jehovah's Witnesses into a worldwide brotherhood. They fully accept what the Bible teaches: that the Kingdom is a real government with laws and authority, and that soon it will govern the entire earth. It already has increasing millions of subjects on earth who are being shaped as the foundation for the civilization to come. Regarding the Kingdom, the prophet Daniel was inspired to write: "The God of heaven will set up a kingdom that will never be brought to ruin. . . . It will crush and put an end to all these kingdoms [now existing], and it itself will stand to times indefinite." (Daniel 2:44) Jesus gave priority to the Kingdom

35. (a) What unifies Jehovah's Witnesses? (b) Is their allegiance to God's Kingdom Scripturally justified?

230

when he instructed: "You must pray, then, this way: 'Our Father in the heavens . . . *Let your kingdom come.*'"—Matthew 6:9, 10.

36 The many events in fulfillment of Bible prophecy since 1914 show that very soon God's heavenly Kingdom will 'crush and put an end to all other governments.' And God wants this fact publicized, as the following important part of the sign shows: "This *good news of the kingdom* will be preached in all the inhabited earth for a witness to all the nations; *and then the end will come.*" (Matthew 24:14) Millions of Jehovah's Witnesses, a worldwide brotherhood, are now fulfilling this prophecy.

37 When the Kingdom has been preached to the extent that God wants, then the world will see, Jesus said, a "great tribulation such as has not occurred since the world's beginning until now, no, nor will occur again." This will culminate in the battle of Armageddon, and it will end Satan's evil influence. It will cleanse the entire earth of wicked nations and men and will open the way for the incoming Paradise where "righteousness is to dwell."—Matthew 24:21; 2 Peter 3:13; Revelation 16:14-16; 12:7-12; 2 Corinthians 4:4.

The Bible has established its credibility as a book inspired by the Creator

38 With so many fulfilled prophecies already to its credit, the Bible has indeed established itself as the book "inspired of God." (2 Timothy 3:16) Accept it, then, "not as the word of men, but, just as it truthfully is, as the word of God." (1 Thessalonians 2:13) Also, since its Author, Jehovah God, is "the One telling from the beginning the finale," you can have complete confidence in prophecies whose fulfillments are yet future. (Isaiah 46:10) And what is to come is truly marvelous. You will be fascinated as you read about it in the next chapter.

---

36. (a) What does God want publicized? (b) Who are doing it?
37. Why will the end of this system of things at Armageddon be good news?
38. (a) What has been established by the Bible's record of fulfilled prophecies? (b) What do those prophecies concerning the future merit?

Chapter 19

An Earthly Paradise Soon to Come

WOULD you like your life to go on indefinitely —full and satisfying? Likely your answer is, Yes. There are so many interesting things to do, fascinating places to see and new things to learn.

Humans cannot achieve ideal conditions, but God can

[2] Yet, seemingly unsolvable problems interfere with our enjoyment of life. For example, there is the comparative shortness of our present life span. Then, too, life is often filled with sickness, sorrow and trouble. So for people to enjoy life to the full, in all its dimensions, the ideal would be to have (1) *surroundings like a paradise,* (2) *complete security,* (3) *absorbing work,* (4) *radiant health* and (5) *unending life.*

[3] But is that asking too much? From the human viewpoint, it certainly is. History has shown that, on their own, humans just cannot bring about such ideal conditions. However, from our Creator's viewpoint those things not only are possible but are inevitable! Why? Because such desirable conditions were part of God's original purpose for this earth. —Psalm 127:1; Matthew 19:26.

Paradise to Be Restored

[4] As we have noted in previous chapters, the first two humans were not like animals. Instead, they

1, 2. (a) What is the normal human desire, but what things interfere with its realization? (b) What conditions would be ideal?
3. Who only can bring about such ideal conditions?
4. What was God's original purpose for this earth?

Paradise surroundings

Complete security

Absorbing work

Radiant health

Unending life

Such ideal conditions would enable us to enjoy life fully

were created completely human. Their original home, Eden, was "a paradise of pleasure." (Genesis 2:8, *Douay Version*) They were "to cultivate it and to take care of it." (Genesis 2:15) Additionally, their role on earth included this very human administrative assignment: "Be fruitful and become many and fill the earth and subdue it." (Genesis 1:28) As their offspring increased, they would have the task of extending the boundaries of this beautiful garden, transforming the whole earth into a paradise. How long was it to last? The Bible consistently notes that the earth will remain "to time indefinite, or forever." (Psalm 104:5; Ecclesiastes 1:4) So the Paradise earth was meant to serve permanently as a delightful home for perfect humans, who would live there forever.—Isaiah 45:11, 12, 18.

233

Those who choose to be independent of the Creator will be cut off

⁵ Though the rebellion in Eden temporarily interrupted the fulfillment of God's purpose, it has not changed that purpose. God has introduced the means for stopping the damage and restoring Paradise. The mechanism for doing this is the Kingdom of God, the heavenly government that Jesus made such a prominent part of his message to mankind. (Matthew 6:10, 33) And we can be certain that the original purpose of God will be accomplished. The all-powerful Creator behind it assures us: "So my word that goes forth from my mouth will prove to be. It will not return to me without results, but it will certainly do that in which I have delighted, and it will have certain success in that for which I have sent it."—Isaiah 55:11.

⁶ In our day it is encouraging to see world events fulfilling "the sign" of "the last days." (Matthew 24: 3-14; 2 Timothy 3:1-5) This indicates that the time is near when God's "word" "will have certain success." This success is certain because the all-powerful God will intervene in human affairs to see that his purposes are accomplished. (Jeremiah 25:

5. Why can we be confident that God's purpose will be realized?
6, 7. (a) How do we know that we are nearing the restoration of Paradise? (b) Who will be preserved through the end of this system of things, and who will not?

234

"Those hoping in Jehovah" will survive

31-33) Very shortly, we can expect to see the fulfillment of the prophetic psalm that says: "Evildoers themselves will be cut off, but those hoping in Jehovah are the ones that will possess the earth. And just a little while longer, and the wicked one will be no more . . . The righteous themselves will possess the earth, *and they will reside forever upon it.*"—Psalm 37:9-11, 29; Matthew 5:5.

⁷ Thus, those who choose to be independent of the Creator will be "cut off." Those who are "hoping in Jehovah" will live through the end of this system and begin the restoration of Paradise. Gradually it will spread until it encompasses the entire earth. This Paradise is so certain to come that with complete confidence Jesus could promise the thief executed alongside him: "Truly I tell you today, You will be with me in Paradise."—Luke 23:43.

235

The Earth Transformed

8 The Bible's description of Paradise is truly breathtaking. For example, it tells of a dramatic change in the condition of the earth itself. You may recall that when expelled from Eden the first humans were told that the ground would bring forth thorns and thistles, and only by the sweat of their face would they be able to grow food from the earth. (Genesis 3:17-19) From then until now it often has been a constant struggle against encroaching deserts, poor soil, drought, weeds, insects, plant diseases and crop failures. Too often famine has won the battle.

9 However, this situation is to be reversed: "The wilderness and the waterless region will exult, and

There will be a dramatic change in the earth itself

8, 9. What reversal of conditions will take place regarding the literal earth?

236

the desert plain will be joyful and blossom as the saffron. . . . For in the wilderness waters will have burst out, and torrents in the desert plain. And the heat-parched ground will have become as a reedy pool, and the thirsty ground as springs of water." "Instead of the thicket of thorns the juniper tree will come up. Instead of the stinging nettle the myrtle tree will come up." (Isaiah 35:1, 6, 7; 55:13) So the working out of God's purpose means that mankind will have the very enjoyable task of transforming the earth into a place of beauty that will forever bring delight to its inhabitants. But it will mean more than just beauty.

Mankind will have the enjoyable task of transforming the earth into a paradise

An End to Poverty

There will be economic security for all

¹⁰ The transformation of vast deserts and drought-affected areas will mean a huge increase in productive land. With the Creator's oversight, man's efforts will succeed in making the earth fruitful as never before: "Jehovah, for his part, will give what is good, and our own land will give its yield." (Psalm 85:12) That "yield" will bring "plenty of grain on the earth; on the top of the mountains there will be an overflow." (Psalm 72:16) Never again will millions starve.—Isaiah 25:6.

¹¹ Too, unemployment will be a thing of the past, eliminated forever. And all will enjoy the fruits of their own labor: "They will certainly plant vineyards and eat their fruitage. . . . they will not plant and someone else do the eating." (Isaiah 65:21, 22) All of this will bring the kind of economic security described in Ezekiel 34:27: "The tree of the field must give its fruitage, and the land itself will give its yield, and they will actually prove to be on their soil *in security.*"

10, 11. How will Jehovah eliminate hunger?

238

Paradise will not be marred by disabilities, sickness or death

¹² But humans also inherently desire a decent home and some ground for planting flowers, trees and gardens. Is it decent housing when millions of people are crammed into huge apartment buildings or run-down slums, or are living on the streets? None of that will exist in the coming Paradise because God has purposed: "They will certainly build houses and have occupancy . . . They will not build and someone else have occupancy." That worldwide building program will be completely successful, and enduring: "The work of their own hands my chosen ones will use to the full. They will not toil for nothing." (Isaiah 65:21-23) Thus, decent housing will not be the privilege of just a wealthy minority, but it will be enjoyed by all who submit to God's rule.

No More Sickness, No More Death

¹³ God's Word also assures us that the satisfying conditions in Paradise will not be marred by disabilities or sickness, or be cut short by death: "No resident will say: 'I am sick.'" (Isaiah 33:24) "[God] will wipe out every tear from their eyes, and death will be no more, neither will mourning nor outcry nor pain be anymore. The former things have passed away."—Revelation 21:4.

---

12. Who will enjoy decent housing in Paradise?
13, 14. What will happen to sickness, handicaps, and even death?

"Let his flesh become fresher than in youth; let him return to the days of his youthful vigor."—Job 33:25

[14] Imagine a world where all sickness and handicaps will be healed! God's Word says: "At that time the eyes of the blind ones will be opened, and the very ears of the deaf ones will be unstopped. At that time the lame one will climb up just as a stag does, and the tongue of the speechless one will cry out in gladness." (Isaiah 35:5, 6) What a marvelous transformation! And imagine, too, the amazing prospect, from that point on, of living as long as God lives—eternally! Never again will death curse mankind, because God "will actually swallow up death *forever*."—Isaiah 25:8.

[15] But what about those who survive the end of this system and who are already old? Will they merely have good health in old age and stay that way forever? No, for God has, and will yet use, the power to reverse the aging process. As the Bible describes it: "Let his flesh become fresher than in youth; let him return to the days of his youthful vigor." (Job 33:25) The aged will gradually return to the perfect manhood and womanhood that Adam and Eve enjoyed in Eden. This process will be one

15. What will happen to old people who survive this system's end?

240

of the results of the "re-creation" about which Jesus spoke.—Matthew 19:28.

Lasting Global Peace

[16] Will Paradise ever be disrupted by war or violence? Not when "the upright are the ones that will reside in the earth, and the blameless are the ones that will be left over in it. As regards the wicked, they will be cut off from the very earth; and as for the treacherous, they will be torn away from it." (Proverbs 2:21, 22) There can be no war or violence when peacebreakers no longer exist.

[17] Why are those who are "left over," after God cuts off the wicked and the treacherous, called "upright" and "blameless"? Because they had already been educated in God's standards for peaceful living and had conformed to those standards. That knowledge of God, and submitting to his laws, is the key to peace in Paradise, for the Bible states: "They will not do any harm or cause any ruin . . . because the earth will certainly be *filled with the knowledge of Jehovah* as the waters are covering the very sea." (Isaiah 11:9) Jesus also said, "They will all be taught by Jehovah," and that those who accept this teaching and live by it will have "everlasting life."—John 6:45-47.

There will be no war or violence in Paradise. All weapons will be destroyed.—Ezekiel 39:9, 10

[18] Happily, this God-oriented, global education will result in a totally peaceful and harmonious world free from crime, prejudice and hatred, free from political divisions and war. Already the value of this education is being demonstrated among millions of Jehovah's Witnesses around the earth. They form an international brotherhood based on love and mutual respect. (John 13:34, 35) Their global peace and unity are unbreakable. Not even persecution or world wars can make them take up arms against their neighbors anywhere in the

16, 17. Why will Paradise not be disrupted by war or violence?
18. Who today are already being educated for peaceful Paradise living?

241

world. Since such global peace and unity can exist even in today's divided world, surely it will be much easier to continue this pattern under God's rule in Paradise.—Matthew 26:52; 1 John 3:10-12.

¹⁹ At the very beginning of the restoration of Paradise, then, earth-wide peace will prevail. And the survivors of God's global war of Armageddon will continue to abide by the words of the prophecy that they are fulfilling right now: "They will not lift up sword, nation against nation, *neither will they learn war anymore.*" That is why the prophecy can add: "They will actually sit, each one under his vine and under his fig tree, and *there will be no one making them tremble.*" (Micah 4:3, 4) For how long? The heartwarming promise is: "To peace there will be no end."—Isaiah 9:7.

²⁰ True, the militarized nations today have stockpiled their armaments as never before. But all of that means nothing to the One whose power created the universe. He tells us what he will soon do to the military weapons of the nations: "Come, you people, behold the activities of Jehovah, how he has set astonishing events on the earth. He is making wars to cease to the extremity of the earth. The bow he breaks apart and does cut the spear in pieces; the wagons he burns in the fire." (Psalm 46:8, 9) The crushing of the nations and their military might will pave the way for lasting global peace in Paradise.—Daniel 2:44; Revelation 19:11-21.

The crushing of the nations and their military might will pave the way for global peace

Peace With the Animal Realm

²¹ To complete the global peace of Paradise, there will be a restoration of the harmony that existed between humans and animals in Eden. (Genesis 1: 26-31) Today, man fears many animals and, at the

19. What fulfillment of prophecy now in progress will continue in Paradise?
20. How will Jehovah deal with the nations and their military equipment?
21, 22. What relationship will be restored between humans and animals?

There will be a restoration of harmony between humans and animals

same time, is a threat to them. But that will not be the case in Paradise. In whatever way God maintained the harmony between man and beast in Eden, he will do in Paradise. Thus man's loving dominion of animals will again be a reality.

²² In this regard the Creator declares: "For them I shall certainly conclude a covenant in that day in connection with the wild beast of the field and with the flying creature of the heavens and the creeping thing of the ground." (Hosea 2:18) With what result? "I will conclude with them *a covenant of peace,* and I shall certainly cause the injurious wild beast to cease out of the land, and they will actually dwell in the wilderness in security and sleep in the forests."—Ezekiel 34:25.

²³ The peace that will exist among humans, and between humans and animals, will also be reflected *within the animal realm:* "The wolf will actually reside for a while with the male lamb, and with the kid the leopard itself will lie down, and the calf and

23. What profound change to come within the animal realm does Isaiah foretell?

243

the maned young lion and the well-fed animal all together; and a mere little boy will be leader over them. And the cow and the bear themselves will feed; together their young ones will lie down. And even the lion will eat straw just like the bull. And the sucking child will certainly play upon the hole of the cobra; and upon the light aperture of a poisonous snake will a weaned child actually put his own hand. They will not do any harm or cause any ruin in all my holy mountain."—Isaiah 11:6-9.

They will find "exquisite delight in the abundance of peace"

[24] What a beautiful description the Bible gives of the total peace that will exist in Paradise! It is no wonder that Psalm 37:11 says of life in that new system: "The meek ones themselves will possess the earth, and they will indeed find their *exquisite delight in the abundance of peace.*"

The Dead Return

[25] The benefits to come in Paradise will flow not just to those who survive the end of this present system of things. Under the rule of God's heavenly Kingdom a most amazing victory will take place—a total victory over death. For not only will inherited death be overcome, but those already dead will come back to life and be given the opportunity to live in Paradise! God's Word guarantees: "There is going to be a resurrection of both the righteous and the unrighteous." (Acts 24:15) What a joyous occasion that will be as, generation after generation, loved ones are brought back from the grave!—Luke 7:11-16; 8:40-56; John 11:38-45.

[26] Jesus said: "The hour is coming in which all those in the memorial tombs will hear his voice and come out, those who did good things to a resurrection of life, those who practiced vile things to a resurrection of judgment." (John 5:28, 29) Yes,

24. How does Psalm 37 describe the peace that will exist in Paradise?
25, 26. (a) What promise does God's Word make regarding the dead? (b) Why is remembering all those who have died no problem for the Creator?

The dead
will come back
to life and be given the
opportunity to live in Paradise!
God's Word guarantees: "There is
going to be a resurrection of both
the righteous and the unrighteous"

those in God's memory will be restored to life. And we should not think that this is too big a task for God. Remember, he created hundreds of billions, yes, trillions, of stars. And the Bible says that he calls all of them "by name." (Isaiah 40:26) The number of people who have lived and died is only a fraction of that. So they and their life patterns can easily be accommodated in God's memory.

[27] All those who are resurrected will be educated in God's righteous standards in a Paradise environment. They will not be hindered by wickedness, suffering or injustice as they were in their past life. If they accept God's rule and conform to his standards, they will be judged worthy of continued life. (Ephesians 4:22-24) So if the thief impaled alongside Jesus is to remain in Paradise, he must change from being a thief to becoming honest. But those who rebel against God's righteous rule will not be allowed to continue living to mar the peace and joy of others. They will receive an adverse judgment. Thus, every person will have a full and fair opportunity to demonstrate whether he really appreciates life on a Paradise earth where "righteousness is to dwell."—2 Peter 3:13.

Immediately ahead of us is a marvelous new era

[28] Together with the Armageddon survivors, the resurrected dead will then enjoy a life of endless fascination. The perfect human brain, with a vast potential for knowledge, will be able to absorb information forever. Think what we will learn about the earth and about the awesome universe with its billions of galaxies! Consider the challenging and satisfying work that we will do in construction, landscaping, gardening, teaching, art, music and many other fields! Hence, life will not be boring or unproductive. Instead, as the Bible foretells, every day in Paradise will be an "exquisite delight." (Psalm 37:11) Thus, immediately ahead of us is the beginning of a marvelous new era.

---

27. What opportunity will all have in Paradise?
28. Thus, what is immediately ahead of us?

Chapter 20

What Choice Will You Make?

THE Paradise to come under God's Kingdom is the kind of news mankind needs. And Jesus prophesied that telling people earth wide about "this good news of the kingdom" would be a feature of the period just 'before the end comes.' (Matthew 24:14) Today, millions of Jehovah's Witnesses are doing just that. They are sharing this good news with other millions who are responding by studying the Bible and associating with them.

2 This vast global educational work that is gathering people from all nations was foretold in the Bible. Isaiah's prophecy said of these last days: 'The worship of Jehovah will become firmly established, and to it people from all the nations must stream. And Jehovah will instruct them about his ways, and they will walk in his paths.'—Isaiah 2: 2-4; see also Isaiah 60:22; Zechariah 8:20-23.

3 The declaring of the Kingdom worldwide is resulting in a clear separation of people. In illustrative language Jesus foretold for our day: "All the nations will be gathered before him, and he will separate people one from another, just as a shepherd separates the sheep from the goats." Those who cooperate with the Creator's purposes are identified as being like sheep. Those who remain independent are said to be like goats. As for their destinies, Jesus said that the "sheep" will reap "everlasting life," but the "goats," "everlasting cutting-off."—Matthew 25:32-46.

Millions are gathering to the true worship of Jehovah

1, 2. (a) How is the "good news" affecting millions of people today? (b) How was this global ingathering foretold?
3. The Kingdom message results in what separation?

Not 'Exchanging the Truth for a Lie'

[4] Bringing our lives into agreement with God's purposes is vital to our future, since with him is "the source of life." (Psalm 36:9) So we should not become ensnared by philosophies that are contrary to reality. Romans 1:25 speaks of "those who exchanged the truth of God for the lie and venerated and rendered sacred service to the creation rather than the One who created." As we have seen, the theory of evolution is contrary to reality, yes, effectively a "lie." Exchanging the facts about the God of Creation for such a "lie" is, as Romans 1:20 states, "inexcusable" in view of the evidence.

Where did the idea of evolution really originate?

[5] Do not be surprised that the theory of evolution has become so widespread in modern times despite the evidence against it. The real message of this belief is that there is no God, that he is unnecessary. From where would such a monumental lie originate? Jesus identified the source when he said: "The Devil . . . is a liar and the father of the lie." —John 8:44.

[6] We need to face the fact that the theory of evolution serves the purposes of Satan. He wants people to imitate his course, and that of Adam and Eve, in rebelling against God. This is especially so now, since the Devil has only "a short period of time" left. (Revelation 12:9-12) Thus, believing in evolution would mean promoting his interests and blinding oneself to the wonderful purposes of the Creator. How, then, should we feel about this? We feel indignant toward those who try to defraud us of money, or even of a few material possessions. We should feel even stronger indignation toward the doctrine of evolution and its originator, since the intent is to defraud us of eternal life.—1 Peter 5:8.

4. (a) If we want to keep living, what is vital? (b) According to the Bible, how must the theory of evolution be classified?
5, 6. (a) Where did the belief in evolution really originate? (b) Why has it become so widespread in our time? (c) How should we feel about this matter?

'All Will Have to Know'

7 Soon, everyone will know that there really is a Creator. He declares: "I shall certainly sanctify my great name, which was being profaned among the nations, . . . *and the nations will have to know that I am Jehovah.*" (Ezekiel 36:23) Yes, everyone will have to know that "Jehovah is God. It is he that has made us, and not we ourselves."—Psalm 100:3.

Soon, all will know that there is a Creator

8 The nations will come to know that Jehovah is the God of Creation when he confronts them shortly. That will happen when he brings an end to the miserable human experiment of trying to be independent of God. At that time the following will take place: "Because of his indignation the earth will rock, and no nations will hold up under his denunciation." "The gods that did not make the very heavens and the earth are the ones who will perish from the earth and from under these heavens." —Jeremiah 10:10, 11; see also Revelation 19:11-21.

9 Thus, in the Paradise to come, the nations, their educational systems and their media will no longer exist. So there will be no teaching of evolution then. Instead, as Isaiah 11:9 shows, "the earth will certainly be *filled with the knowledge of Jehovah* as the waters are covering the very sea." Every person will be educated to know the Creator intimately. They will marvel at how he has worked out his purposes in the past. They will see his future works in Paradise and be thrilled by them. And among those awesome works will be the resurrection. That will demonstrate conclusively that God did create humans. Why? Because his ability to re-create billions of dead persons surely will prove that he was able to create the first human pair.

The resurrection will prove that God did create humans

7. What does the Creator say he will do regarding his existence and his name?
8. How will the nations be confronted by Jehovah shortly?
9. (a) Why will there be no teaching of evolution in Paradise? (b) What awesome display of Jehovah's ability will prove that he created humans?

249

Making a Choice

¹⁰ No, the future will not be determined by some chance evolutionary process. The future has already been determined by the Creator. It is *his* purposes that will be realized, not those of any human or Devil. (Isaiah 46:9-11) In view of this, the questions that each one of us must answer are: Where do I stand? Do I want to live forever in a righteous Paradise? If I do, am I meeting God's requirements for survival?

The future has already been determined

¹¹ If we want to live forever in Paradise, then the Bible shows that we must follow the example of those who respect the Creator, his purposes and his laws. It counsels: "Watch the blameless one and keep the upright one in sight, for the future of that man will be peaceful. But the transgressors themselves will certainly be annihilated together; the future of wicked people will indeed be cut off." —Psalm 37:37, 38.

¹² God gave us the freedom to choose whether we would serve him or not. And while he will not force humans to be obedient, neither will he allow wickedness, suffering and injustice to continue indefinitely. Nor will he allow anyone to keep on living who would upset the peace and happiness in his Paradise to come. That is why he now invites people to use their free choice to serve him. Those who do so will see this unsatisfactory world end, and then they will have the great joy of helping to transform the earth into a paradise.—Psalm 37:34.

How will we use our freedom of choice?

¹³ True, many people do not want to conform to Jehovah's requirements. That is their responsibility, and great loss. (Ezekiel 33:9) But is it your

10. In view of the fact that Jehovah already has determined the future, what questions do we need to answer?
11. Whose example should we follow if we want to live in Paradise?
12. (a) Although humans do have freedom of choice, what will God not allow to continue? (b) What awaits those who use their free choice to serve God?
13. If we want "the real life," what should we do?

250

desire to "get a firm hold on the real life" to come? (1 Timothy 6:19) If so, Jesus showed what to do when he said in prayer to God: "This means everlasting life, their taking in knowledge of you, the only true God, and of the one whom you sent forth, Jesus Christ."—John 17:3.

A glorious prospect is ahead for those who make the right choice

¹⁴ So the wise and urgent course to take, while there is yet time, is to learn the Creator's will and sincerely try to do it. His inspired Word urges: "Before there comes upon you the day of Jehovah's anger, seek Jehovah, all you meek ones of the earth, who have practiced His own judicial decision. Seek righteousness, seek meekness. Probably you may be concealed in the day of Jehovah's anger." —Zephaniah 2:2, 3.

¹⁵ May you prove to be such a meek person, humbly submitting to God's will. If you do, what then? "The world is passing away," the Bible says, "but he that does the will of God remains forever." (1 John 2:17) What a glorious prospect—living forever on a Paradise earth—if you make the right choice!

---

14. What wise and urgent course should we take?
15. What glorious prospect awaits meek persons?

References Listed by Chapter

Chapter 1
Life—How Did It Start?

1. *Cosmos,* by Carl Sagan, 1980, p. 328.
2. *Ibid.,* p. 231.
3. *The Origin of Species,* by Charles Darwin, Mentor edition, 1958, p. 450.

Chapter 2
Disagreements About Evolution —Why?

1. *Discover,* "The Tortoise or the Hare?" by James Gorman, October 1980, p. 88.
2. *The Neck of the Giraffe,* by Francis Hitching, 1982, p. 12.
3. *The Enterprise,* Riverside, California, "Macroevolution Theory Stirs Hottest Debate Since Darwin," by Boyce Rensberger, November 14, 1980, p. E9; *Science,* "Evolutionary Theory Under Fire," by Roger Lewin, November 21, 1980, pp. 883-887.
4. *Natural History,* "Evolutionary Housecleaning," by Niles Eldredge, February 1982, pp. 78, 81.
5. *The Star,* Johannesburg, "The Evolution of a Theory," by Christopher Booker, April 20, 1982, p. 19.
6. *The Neck of the Giraffe,* pp. 7, 8.
7. *New Scientist,* "Darwin's Theory: An Exercise in Science," by Michael Ruse, June 25, 1981, p. 828.
8. *The Enchanted Loom: Mind in the Universe,* by Robert Jastrow, 1981, p. 19.
9. *The Origin of Species,* by Charles Darwin, 1902 edition, Part One, p. 250.
10. *The Enchanted Loom,* p. 96.
11. *Ibid.,* pp. 98, 100.
12. *Field Museum of Natural History Bulletin,* Chicago, "Conflicts Between Darwin and Paleontology," by David M. Raup, January 1979, pp. 22, 23, 25.
13. *The New Evolutionary Timetable,* by Steven M. Stanley, 1981, pp. 71, 77.
14. *The Enterprise,* November 14, 1980, p. E9.
15. *Science Digest,* "Miracle Mutations," by John Gliedman, February 1982, p. 92.
16. *The World Book Encyclopedia,* 1982, Vol. 6, p. 335.
17. *The New York Times,* "Theory of Rapid Evolution Attacked," by Bayard Webster, July 9, 1981, p. B11.
18. *Harper's,* "Darwin's Mistake," by Tom Bethell, February 1976, pp. 72, 75.
19. *The Neck of the Giraffe,* pp. 103, 107, 108, 117.
20. *The Guardian,* London, "Beginning to Have Doubts," by John Durant, December 4, 1980, p. 15.
a. *The Origin of Species,* introduction by W. R. Thompson, 1956 edition, p. xxii.
b. *The New York Times,* "Computer Scientists Stymied in Their Quest to Match Human Vision," by William J. Broad, September 25, 1984, p. C1.
c. *Field Museum of Natural History Bulletin,* January 1979, p. 25.

Chapter 3
What Does Genesis Say?

1. *Old Testament Word Studies,* by William Wilson, 1978, p. 109.
2. *Putnam's Geology,* by Edwin E. Larson and Peter W. Birkeland, 1982, p. 66.
3. *The Illustrated Bible Dictionary,* Tyndale House Publishers, 1980, Part 1, p. 335.
4. *Aid to Bible Understanding,* published by the Watchtower Bible and Tract Society of New York, Inc., 1971, p. 393.
a. *Ibid.,* pp. 392, 393.
b. *The Lamp,* "The Worlds of Wallace Pratt," by W. L. Copithorne, Fall 1971, p. 14.

Chapter 4
Could Life Originate by Chance?

1. *The Origin of Species,* by Charles Darwin, Mentor edition, 1958, p. 450.
2. *The Selfish Gene,* by Richard Dawkins, 1976, p. 16.
3. *Ibid.,* p. ix.
4. *The Neck of the Giraffe,* by Francis Hitching, 1982, p. 68.
5. *Evolution From Space,* by Fred Hoyle and Chandra Wickramasinghe, 1981, p. 8.
6. *The Origins of Life on the Earth,* by Stanley L. Miller and Leslie E. Orgel, 1974, p. 33.
7. *The Neck of the Giraffe,* p. 65.
8. *Ibid.*
9. *Ibid.*
10. *Scientific American,* "Chemical Evolution and the Origin of Life," by Richard E. Dickerson, September 1978, p. 75.
11. *Scientific American,* "The Origin of Life," by George Wald, August 1954, pp. 49, 50.
12. *The Origin of Life,* by John D. Bernal, 1967, p. 144.
13. *Evolution From Space,* p. 24.
14. *New Scientist,* "Darwinism at the Very Beginning of Life," by Leslie Orgel, April 15, 1982, p. 151.
15. *Evolution From Space,* p. 27.
16. *The Neck of the Giraffe,* p. 66.
17. *Scientific American,* September 1978, p. 73.
18. *The Sciences,* "The Creationist Revival," by Joel Gurin, April 1981, p. 17.
19. *Scientific American,* September 1978, p. 85.
20. *New Scientist,* April 15, 1982, p. 151.
21. *Life Itself, Its Origin and Nature,* by Francis Crick, 1981, p. 71.
22. *The Plants,* by Frits W. Went, 1963, p. 60.
23. *Evolution From Space,* pp. 30, 31.
24. *Ibid.,* p. 130.
25. *The Selfish Gene,* p. 14.
26. *Evolution From Space,* p. 31.
27. *Scientific American,* August 1954, p. 46.
28. *The Immense Journey,* by Loren Eiseley, 1957, p. 200.
29. *Ibid.,* p. 199.
30. *Physics Bulletin,* "A Physicist Looks at Evolution," by H. S. Lipson, 1980, Vol. 31, p. 138.
31. *Daily Express,* London, "There Must Be a God," by Geoffrey Levy, August 14, 1981, p. 28.
32. *The Enchanted Loom: Mind in the Universe,* by Robert Jastrow, 1981, p. 19.
a. *Life Itself,* p. 71.
b. *National Geographic,* "The Awesome Worlds Within a Cell," by Rick Gore, September 1976, pp. 357, 358, 360.
c. *Newsweek,* "The Secrets of the Human Cell," by Peter Gwynne, Sharon Begley and Mary Hager, August 20, 1979, p. 48.
d. *The Limitations of Science,* by J. W. N. Sullivan, 1933, p. 95.
e. *Reader's Digest,* January 1963, p. 92.
f. *Scientific American,* August 1954, p. 46.

g. *Life Itself,* p. 88.
h. *Evolution From Space,* p. 24.

Chapter 5
Letting the Fossil Record Speak

1. *Processes of Organic Evolution,* by G. Ledyard Stebbins, 1971, p. 1.
2. *Genetics and the Origin of Species,* by Theodosius Dobzhansky, 1951, p. 4.
3. *The Origin of Species,* by Charles Darwin, 1902 edition, Part Two, p. 54.
4. *New Scientist,* book review by Tom Kemp of *The New Evolutionary Timetable* by Steven M. Stanley, February 4, 1982, p. 320.
5. *The Origin of Species,* Part Two, p. 55.
6. *Ibid.,* p. 83.
7. *Ibid.,* p. 55.
8. *Ibid.,* pp. 83, 88, 91, 92.
9. *Ibid.,* pp. 94, 296.
10. *Processes of Organic Evolution,* p. 136.
11. *New Scientist,* January 15, 1981, p. 129.
12. *A Guide to Earth History,* by Richard Carrington, 1956, p. 48.
13. *The New Evolutionary Timetable,* by Steven M. Stanley, 1981, p. 6.
14. *A View of Life,* by Salvador E. Luria, Stephen Jay Gould, Sam Singer, 1981, p. 642.
15. *Synthetische Artbildung* (The Synthetic Origin of Species), by Heribert Nilsson, 1953, p. 1212.
16. *Red Giants and White Dwarfs,* by Robert Jastrow, 1979, p. 97.
17. *Evolution From Space,* by Fred Hoyle and Chandra Wickramasinghe, 1981, p. 8.
18. *Red Giants and White Dwarfs,* p. 249.
19. *The Enchanted Loom: Mind in the Universe,* by Robert Jastrow, 1981, p. 23.
20. *A View of Life,* pp. 638, 649.
21. *The Origin of Species,* Part Two, p. 90.
22. *Natural History,* "Darwin and the Fossil Record," by Alfred S. Romer, October 1959, pp. 466, 467.
23. *A View of Life,* p. 651.
24. Kentish *Times,* England, "Scientist Rejects Evolution," December 11, 1975, p. 4.
25. *Liberty,* "Evolution or Creation?" by Harold G. Coffin, September/October 1975, p. 12.
26. *The New Evolutionary Timetable,* p. xv.
27. *The New York Times,* "Prehistoric Gnat," October 3, 1982, Section 1, p. 49.
28. *The Globe and Mail,* Toronto, "That's Life," October 5, 1982, p. 6.
29. *Discover,* "The Tortoise or the Hare?" by James Gorman, October 1980, p. 89.
30. *Field Museum of Natural History Bulletin,* Chicago, "Conflicts Between Darwin and Paleontology," by David M. Raup, January 1979, p. 23.
31. *New Scientist,* February 4, 1982, p. 320.
32. *Processes of Organic Evolution,* p. 147.
33. *The New Evolutionary Timetable,* p. 95.
34. *Should Evolution be Taught?* by John N. Moore, 1970, pp. 9, 14, 24; *New Scientist,* "Letters," September 15, 1983, p. 798.
35. *On Growth and Form,* by D'Arcy Thompson, 1959, Vol. II, pp. 1093, 1094.
36. *The World Book Encyclopedia,* 1982, Vol. 6, p. 333.
37. *Encyclopædia Britannica,* 1976, Macropædia, Vol. 7, p. 13.
38. *The Neck of the Giraffe,* by Francis Hitching, 1982, p. 31.

39. *The New Evolutionary Timetable,* pp. 4, 96.
40. *Order: In Life,* by Edmund Samuel, 1972, p. 120.
41. *Liberty,* September/October 1975, p. 14.
42. *Cosmos,* by Carl Sagan, 1980, p. 29.
a. *The Enchanted Loom,* p. 29.
b. *The New Evolutionary Timetable,* pp. 4, 5.
c. *The World We Live In,* by Lincoln Barnett, 1955, p. 93.
d. *Red Giants and White Dwarfs,* p. 224.
e. *Science,* February 23, 1973, p. 789.
f. *Red Giants and White Dwarfs,* p. 249.
g. *The Natural History of Palms,* by E. J. H. Corner, 1966, p. 254.
h. *Encyclopædia Britannica,* 1976, Macropædia, Vol. 7, p. 565.
i. *The Insects,* by Peter Farb, 1962, p. 14.
j. *Encyclopædia Britannica,* 1976, Macropædia, Vol. 7, p. 567.
k. *Marvels & Mysteries of Our Animal World,* by The Reader's Digest Association, 1964, p. 25.
l. *The Fishes,* by F. D. Ommanney, 1964, p. 64.
m. *The Reptiles,* by Archie Carr, 1963, p. 37.
n. *Ibid.,* p. 41.
o. *The Mammals,* by Richard Carrington, 1963, p. 37.
p. *Processes of Organic Evolution,* p. 146.
q. *The World Book Encyclopedia,* 1982, Vol. 2, p. 291.
r. *The Primates,* by Sarel Eimerl and Irven DeVore, 1965, p. 15.
s. *Science Digest,* "The Water People," by Lyall Watson, May 1982, p. 44.
t. *Science Digest,* "Miracle Mutations," by John Gliedman, February 1982, p. 90.
u. *The New Evolutionary Timetable,* p. 5.

Chapter 6
Huge Gulfs—Can Evolution Bridge Them?
1. *The Neck of the Giraffe,* by Francis Hitching, 1982, p. 19.
2. *Ibid.,* p. 20.
3. *The Origin of Vertebrates,* by N. J. Berrill, 1955, p. 10.
4. *The Fishes,* by F. D. Ommanney, 1964, p. 65.
5. *Life on Earth,* by David Attenborough, 1979, p. 137.
6. *The Reptiles,* by Archie Carr, 1963, p. 36.
7. *Ibid.,* p. 37.
8. *Red Giants and White Dwarfs,* by Robert Jastrow, 1979, p. 253.
9. *Human Destiny,* by Lecomte du Noüy, 1947, p. 72.
10. *The Birds,* by Roger Tory Peterson, 1963, p. 34.
11. *Ibid.*
12. *The Neck of the Giraffe,* pp. 34, 35; *Science,* "Feathers of Archaeopteryx: Asymmetric Vanes Indicate Aerodynamic Function," by Alan Feduccia and Harrison B. Tordoff, March 9, 1979, pp. 1021, 1022.
13. *Evolution, Genetics, and Man,* by Theodosius Dobzhansky, 1955, p. 293.
14. *Ibid.,* p. 295.
15. *Populations, Species, and Evolution,* by Ernst Mayr, 1970, p. 375.
16. *The Brain: The Last Frontier,* by Richard M. Restak, 1979, p. 162.
17. *Evolution From Space,* by Fred Hoyle and Chandra Wickramasinghe, 1981, p. 111.

Chapter 7
"Ape-Men"—What Were They?
1. *Science 81,* "How Ape Became Man," by Donald C. Johanson and Maitland A. Edey, April 1981, p. 45.
2. *Lucy: The Beginnings of Humankind,* by Donald C. Johanson and Maitland A. Edey, 1981, p. 31.
3. *Boston Magazine,* "Stephen Jay Gould: Defending Darwin," by Carl Oglesby, February 1981, p. 52.
4. *Lucy,* p. 27.
5. *The Bulletin of the Atomic Scientists,* "Fifty Years of Studies on Human Evolution," by Sherwood Washburn, May 1982, pp. 37, 41.
6. *Spectator,* The University of Iowa, April 1973, p. 4.
7. *New Scientist,* "Whatever Happened to Zinjanthropus?" by John Reader, March 26, 1981, p. 802.
8. *Origins,* by Richard E. Leakey and Roger Lewin, 1977, p. 55.
9. *Science,* "The Politics of Paleoanthropology," by Constance Holden, August 14, 1981, p. 737.
10. *Newsweek,* "Bones and Prima Donnas," by Peter Gwynne, John Carey and Lea Donosky, February 16, 1981, p. 77.
11. *The New York Times,* "How Old Is Man?" by Nicholas Wade, October 4, 1982, p. A18.
12. *Science Digest,* "The Water People," by Lyall Watson, May 1982, p. 44.
13. *The Mismeasure of Man,* by Stephen Jay Gould, 1981, p. 324.
14. *The Universe Within,* by Morton Hunt, 1982, p. 45.
15. *Science Digest,* "Miracle Mutations," by John Gliedman, February 1982, p. 91.
16. *Newsweek,* "Is Man a Subtle Accident?" by Jerry Adler and John Carey, November 3, 1980, p. 95.
17. *Science 81,* "Human Evolution: Smooth or Jumpy?" September 1981, p. 7.
18. *Journal of the Royal College of Surgeons of Edinburgh,* "Myths and Methods in Anatomy," by Solly Zuckerman, January 1966, p. 90.
19. *National Geographic,* "Skull 1470," by Richard E. Leakey, June 1973, p. 819.
20. *The Boston Globe,* "He's Shaking Mankind's Family Tree," by Joel N. Shurkin, December 4, 1973, p. 1.
21. *The New York Times,* October 4, 1982, p. A18.
22. *Discover,* book review by James Gorman of *The Myths of Human Evolution* by Niles Eldredge and Ian Tattersall, January 1983, pp. 83, 84.
23. *The Biology of Race,* by James C. King, 1971, pp. 135, 151.
24. *Science Digest,* "Anthro Art," April 1981, p. 41.
25. *Lucy,* p. 286.
26. *New Scientist,* book review of *Not From the Apes: Man's Origins and Evolution* by Björn Kurtén, August 3, 1972, p. 259.
27. *The Neck of the Giraffe,* by Francis Hitching, 1982, p. 204.
28. *Man, God and Magic,* by Ivar Lissner, 1961, p. 304.
29. *Missing Links,* by John Reader, 1981, pp. 109, 110; *Hen's Teeth and Horse's Toes,* by Stephen Jay Gould, 1983, pp. 201-226.
30. *Lucy,* p. 315.
31. *Origins,* p. 40.
32. *Time,* "Just a Nasty Little Thing," February 18, 1980, p. 58.
33. *The New York Times,* "Monkeylike Af-

rican Primate Called Common Ancestor of Man and Apes," by Bayard Webster, February 7, 1980, p. A14; "Fossils Bolster a Theory on Man's Earliest Ancestor," by Bayard Webster, January 1, 1984, Section 1, p. 16.
34. *Origins,* p. 52.
35. *Ibid.,* p. 56.
36. *Ibid.,* p. 67.
37. *The New York Times,* "Time to Revise the Family Tree?" February 14, 1982, p. E7.
38. *New Scientist,* "Jive Talking," by John Gribbin, June 24, 1982, p. 873.
39. *Natural History,* "False Start of the Human Parade," by Adrienne L. Zihlman and Jerold M. Lowenstein, August/September 1979, p. 86.
40. *The Social Contract,* by Robert Ardrey, 1970, p. 299.
41. *The New York Times,* "Bone Traces Man Back 5 Million Years," by Robert Reinhold, February 19, 1971, p. 1.
42. *Man, Time, and Fossils,* by Ruth Moore, 1961, pp. 5, 6, 316.
43. *The New Evolutionary Timetable,* by Steven M. Stanley, 1981, p. 142.
44. *Journal of the Royal College of Surgeons of Edinburgh,* January 1966, p. 93.
45. *Beyond the Ivory Tower,* by Solly Zuckerman, 1970, p. 90.
46. *Lucy,* p. 38.
47. *Origins,* p. 86.
48. *The Enchanted Loom: Mind in the Universe,* by Robert Jastrow, 1981, p. 114.
49. *New Scientist,* "Trees Have Made Man Upright," by Jeremy Cherfas, January 20, 1983, p. 172.
50. *Encyclopædia Britannica,* 1976, Macropædia, Vol. 8, p. 1032.
51. *Ice,* by Fred Hoyle, 1981, p. 35.
52. *Lucy,* p. 29.
53. *Popular Science,* "How Old Is It?" by Robert Gannon, November 1979, p. 81.
54. *Seattle Post-Intelligencer,* "Radiocarbon Dating Wrong," January 18, 1976, p. C8.
55. *The Fate of the Earth,* by Jonathan Schell, 1982, p. 181.
56. *The Last Two Million Years,* by The Reader's Digest Association, 1974, pp. 9, 29.
57. *Science,* "Radiocarbon Dating," by W. F. Libby, March 3, 1961, p. 624.
58. *Esquire,* book review by Malcolm Muggeridge of *The Ascent of Man* by Jacob Bronowski, July 1974, p. 53.

Chapter 8
Mutations—A Basis for Evolution?
1. *The World Book Encyclopedia,* 1982, Vol. 13, p. 809.
2. *The New Evolutionary Timetable,* by Steven M. Stanley, 1981, p. 65.
3. *Chromosomes and Genes,* by Peo C. Koller, 1971, p. 127.
4. *Red Giants and White Dwarfs,* by Robert Jastrow, 1979, p. 250.
5. *Cosmos,* by Carl Sagan, 1980, p. 27.
6. *Science Digest,* "Miracle Mutations," by John Gliedman, February 1982, p. 92.
7. *Encyclopedia Americana,* 1977, Vol. 10, p. 742.
8. *Cosmos,* p. 31.
9. *Chromosomes and Genes,* p. 127.
10. *Encyclopædia Britannica,* 1959, Vol. 22, p. 989.
11. *The Toronto Star,* "Crusade to Unravel Life's Sweet Mystery," by Helen Bullock, December 19, 1981, p. A13.

12. *Encyclopedia Americana,* 1977, Vol. 10, p. 742.
13. *Processes of Organic Evolution,* by G. Ledyard Stebbins, 1971, pp. 24, 25.
14. *The Wellsprings of Life,* by Isaac Asimov, 1960, p. 139.
15. *Heredity and the Nature of Man,* by Theodosius Dobzhansky, 1964, p. 126.
16. *The World Book Encyclopedia,* 1982, Vol. 6, p. 332.
17. *Heredity and the Nature of Man,* p. 126.
18. *Scientific American,* "Inducible Repair of DNA," by Paul Howard-Flanders, November 1981, p. 72.
19. *Darwin Retried,* by Norman Macbeth, 1971, p. 33.
20. *The International Wildlife Encyclopedia,* 1970, Vol. 20, p. 2706.
21. *Red Giants and White Dwarfs,* p. 235.
22. *On Call,* July 3, 1972, p. 9.
23. *Evolution From Space,* by Fred Hoyle and Chandra Wickramasinghe, 1981, p. 5.
24. *On Call,* July 3, 1972, pp. 8, 9.
25. *Science,* "Evolutionary Theory Under Fire," by Roger Lewin, November 21, 1980, p. 884.
26. *Molecules to Living Cells,* "Simple Inorganic Molecules to Complex Free-Living Cells," *Scientific American,* Section I, introduction by Philip C. Hanawalt, 1980, p. 3.
27. *Symbiosis in Cell Evolution,* by Lynn Margulis, 1981, p. 87.
28. *Scientific American,* "The Genetic Control of the Shape of a Virus," by Edouard Kellenberger, December 1966, p. 32.
29. *Los Angeles Times,* "Fishing for Evolution's Answer," by Irving S. Bengelsdorf, November 2, 1967.
30. *The Orion Book of Evolution,* by Jean Rostand, 1961, p. 79.
31. *Science Today,* "Evolution," by C. H. Waddington, 1961, p. 38.
32. *On Chromosomes, Mutations, and Phylogeny,* by John N. Moore, December 27, 1971, p. 5.

Chapter 9
Our Awesome Universe
1. *National Geographic,* "The Incredible Universe," by Kenneth F. Weaver, May 1974, p. 589.
2. *World Press Review,* quoting *Maclean's* magazine, "Astronomy's Coming Breakthroughs," by Terence Dickinson, March 1982, p. 35.
3. *National Geographic,* May 1974, p. 592.
4. *Discover,* "View From the Corner of the Eye," by Lewis Thomas, April 1981, p. 69.
5. *Webster's New Collegiate Dictionary,* 1981, Eighth edition, p. 254.
6. *Reader's Digest,* July 1962, p. 38.
7. *The New York Times Magazine,* "The Universe and Dr. Hawking," by Michael Harwood, January 23, 1983, p. 53.
8. *National Enquirer,* February 10, 1976.
9. *Science News,* "The Universe: Chaotic or Bioselective?" by Dietrick E. Thomsen, August 24 and 31, 1974, p. 124.
10. *Cosmos,* by Carl Sagan, 1980, p. 21.
11. *The Universe,* by Josip Kleczek, 1976, Vol. 11, p. 17.
12. *Life Itself,* by Francis Crick, 1981, p. 30.
13. *The Enchanted Loom: Mind in the Universe,* by Robert Jastrow, p. 5.
14. *New Scientist,* "Taking the Lid Off Cosmology," by John Gribbin, August 16, 1979, p. 506.

Chapter 10
Evidence From a Unique Planet
1. *Science,* "The Uniqueness of the Earth's Climate," by Allen L. Hammond, January 24, 1975, p. 245.
2. *Discover,* "View From the Corner of the Eye," by Lewis Thomas, April 1981, p. 69.
3. *The Earth,* by Arthur Beiser, 1963, p. 10.
4. *Scientific American,* "Energy in the Universe," by Freeman J. Dyson, September 1971, p. 59.
5. *Science News,* "The Universe: Chaotic or Bioselective?" by Dietrick E. Thomsen, August 24 and 31, 1974, p. 124.
6. *The New England Journal of Medicine,* September 13, 1973, Vol. 289, p. 577.

Chapter 11
The Amazing Design of Living Things
1. *The Origin of Species,* by Charles Darwin, Mentor edition, 1958, p. 90.
2. *Discover,* "Evolution as Fact and Theory," by Stephen Jay Gould, May 1981, p. 35.
3. *The Great Evolution Mystery,* by Gordon Rattray Taylor, 1983, p. 233.
4. *Field Museum of Natural History Bulletin,* "Conflicts Between Darwin and Paleontology," by David M. Raup, January 1979, p. 26.
5. *Scientific American,* "Adaptation," by Richard Lewontin, September 1978, p. 213.
6. *The Center of Life,* by L. L. Larison Cudmore, 1977, pp. 13, 14.
7. *The River of Life,* by Rutherford Platt, 1956, p. 116.
8. *The Center of Life,* pp. 16, 17.
9. *Biology,* by Helena Curtis, 1983, Fourth edition, p. 484.
10. *Life on Earth,* by David Attenborough, 1979, pp. 26, 29.
11. *Science Digest,* "Earth's Odd Couples," by Mary Batten, November/December 1980, p. 66.
12. *The Center of Life,* pp. 137, 138.
13. *The New York Times,* "Materialism Hit by Dr. Millikan," April 30, 1948, p. 21.
a. *The Audubon Society Encyclopedia of North American Birds,* by John K. Terres, 1980, pp. 833, 834.

Chapter 12
Who Did It First?
1. *The Center of Life,* by L. L. Larison Cudmore, 1977, pp. 23, 24.
2. *How Life Learned to Live,* by Helmut Tributsch, 1982, p. 204.
3. *The Atlantic Monthly,* "Debating the Unknowable," by Lewis Thomas, July 1981, p. 49.
4. *Science News Letter,* August 23/30, 1975, p. 126.
5. *How Life Learned to Live,* p. 172.
6. *Smithsonian,* "Bacteria's Motors Work in Forward, Reverse and 'Twiddle,'" by Leo Janos, September 1983, p. 134.
7. *How Life Learned to Live,* p. 68.

Chapter 13
Instinct—Wisdom Programmed Before Birth
1. *The Origin of Species,* by Charles Darwin, Mentor edition, 1958, p. 228.
2. *The Great Evolution Mystery,* by Gordon Rattray Taylor, 1983, pp. 221, 222.
3. *The Birds,* by Roger Tory Peterson, 1963, p. 106.

4. *A View of Life,* by Salvador E. Luria, Stephen Jay Gould and Sam Singer, 1981, p. 556.
5. *Life on Earth,* by David Attenborough, 1979, p. 184.
6. *The Story of Pollination,* by B. J. D. Meeuse, 1961, p. 171.
7. *How Life Learned to Live,* by Helmut Tributsch, 1982, p. 15.
a. *The Great Evolution Mystery,* p. 221.

Chapter 14
The Human Miracle
1. *The Brain: The Last Frontier,* by Richard M. Restak, 1979, p. 390.
2. *The Universe Within,* by Morton Hunt, 1982, p. 44.
3. *Scientific American,* "Thinking About the Brain," by Francis Crick, September 1979, pp. 229, 230.
4. *Ibid.,* "The Development of the Brain," by W. Maxwell Cowan, p. 131.
5. *Ibid.,* "The Brain," by David H. Hubel, p. 52.
6. *The Brain: The Last Frontier,* p. 158.
7. *The Brain: Mystery of Matter and Mind,* by Jack Fincher, 1981, p. 37.
8. *Cosmos,* by Carl Sagan, 1980, p. 278.
9. *The Universe Within,* p. 44.
10. *Scientific American,* "Specializations of the Human Brain," by Norman Geschwind, September 1979, p. 180.
11. *The Universe Within,* p. 166.
12. *Ibid.,* pp. 227-229.
13. *The Brain: Mystery of Matter and Mind,* p. 59.
14. *The Brain: The Last Frontier,* p. 331.
15. *Ibid.*
16. *Science News Letter,* "List 2,000 Languages," September 3, 1955, p. 148.
17. *Man: His First Million Years,* by Ashley Montagu, 1962, p. 102.
18. *The Brain: The Last Frontier,* pp. 332, 333.
19. *Programs of the Brain,* by J. Z. Young, 1978, p. 186.
20. *The Brain: Mystery of Matter and Mind,* p. 53.
21. *Encyclopædia Britannica,* 1976, Macropædia, Vol. 12, p. 998.
22. *The Brain: The Last Frontier,* pp. 59, 69.
23. *Cosmos,* p. 278.
24. *The Selfish Gene,* by Richard Dawkins, 1976, pp. 4, 215.
25. *Cosmos,* p. 278.
a. *Why We Believe in Creation Not Evolution,* by Fred J. Meldau, 1964, p. 238.
b. *Ibid.*
c. *Scientific American,* September 1979, p. 219.
d. *Los Angeles Times,* "Network in Human Brain Shames Man-Made Variety," by Irving S. Bengelsdorf, October 8, 1967.
e. *The Universe Within,* p. 85.
f. *The Brain: The Last Frontier,* p. 162.
g. *Ibid.,* pp. 58, 59.
h. *Reader's Digest,* "Thoughts of a Brain Surgeon," by Robert J. White, September 1978, pp. 99, 100.

Chapter 15
Why Do Many Accept Evolution?
1. *American Laboratory,* "The Editor's Page," by Donald F. Calbreath, November 1980, p. 10.
2. *New Scientist,* "The Necessity of Darwinism," by Richard Dawkins, April 15, 1982, p. 130.
3. *Impact,* September 1981, p. ii.

4. *New Scientist,* "Letters," May 13, 1982, p. 450.
5. *A View of Life,* by Salvador E. Luria, Stephen Jay Gould and Sam Singer, 1981, p. 574.
6. *Ibid.,* p. 575.
7. *Missing Links,* by John Reader, 1981, pp. 10, 81, 209, 226.
8. *The Origin of Species,* by Charles Darwin, 1956 edition, introduction by W. R. Thompson, pp. viii, xii.
9. *Ibid.,* pp. xxi, xxii.
10. *The Commercial Appeal,* Memphis, Tennessee, "Darwin Issue Draws Rebuff of Professor," by Arthur J. Snider, September 9, 1973, Section 1, p. 21.
11. *Evolution From Space,* by Fred Hoyle and Chandra Wickramasinghe, 1981, p. 137.
12. *Hospital Practice,* September 1981, p. 17.
13. *New Catholic Encyclopedia,* 1967, Vol. V, p. 694.
14. *Nature,* "Twelve Wise Men at the Vatican," by J. M. Lowenstein, September 30, 1982, p. 395.

Chapter 17
Can You Trust the Bible?

1. *Free Inquiry,* "The Bible as a Political Weapon," by Gerald Larue, Summer 1983, p. 39.
2. *Scientific Monthly,* "Geology and Health," by Harry V. Warren, June 1954, p. 396.
3. *Cook's Commentary,* edited by F. C. Cook, 1878, Vol. IV, p. 96.
4. *Encyclopedia Americana,* 1977, Vol. 9, p. 553.
5. *The World Book Encyclopedia,* 1984, Vol. 20, p. 136.
6. *God and the Astronomers,* by Robert Jastrow, 1978, pp. 11, 14.
7. *Ibid.,* p. 16.
8. *The Saturday Evening Post,* "Riddle of the Frozen Giants," by Ivan T. Sanderson, January 16, 1960, pp. 82, 83.
9. *The New Dictionary of Thoughts,* 1954, originally compiled by Tryon Edwards. Revised by C. N. Catrevas and Jonathan Edwards, p. 534.
10. *The Physician Examines the Bible,* by C. Raimer Smith, 1950, p. 354.
11. *The Papyrus Ebers,* by C. P. Bryan, 1931, pp. 73, 91, 92.
12. *None of These Diseases,* by S. I. McMillen, 1963, p. 23.
13. *Encyclopedia Americana,* 1956, Vol. 18, p. 582b.
14. *The Lancet,* "Mental Health and Spiritual Values," by Geoffrey Vickers, March 11, 1955, p. 524.
15. *Today's Health,* "How to Avoid Harmful Stress," by J. D. Ratcliff, July 1970, p. 43.
16. *A Few Buttons Missing,* by James T. Fisher and Lowell S. Hawley, 1951, p. 273.
17. *Abraham, Recent Discoveries and Hebrew Origins,* by Leonard Woolley, 1935, p. 22.
18. *The Pentateuch and Haftorahs,* "Exodus," edited by J. H. Hertz, 1951, p. 106.
19. *From the Stone Age to Christianity,* by William Foxwell Albright, 1940, pp. 192, 193.
20. *The Pentateuch and Haftorahs,* p. 106.
21. *Digging Up the Bible,* by Moshe Pearlman, 1980, p. 85.
22. *Ancient Near Eastern Texts Relating to the Old Testament,* edited by James B. Pritchard, 1969, pp. 284, 285.
23. *Digging Up the Bible,* p. 85.
24. *Ibid.*
25. *Ancient Near Eastern Texts,* p. 288.
26. *Universal Jewish History,* by Philip Biberfeld, 1948, Vol. I, p. 27.
27. *Nabonidus and Belshazzar,* by Raymond Philip Dougherty, 1929, p. 200.
28. *The Sun,* Baltimore, Maryland, March 24, 1980, "Unearthing Pontius Pilate," by Michael J. Howard, pp. B1, B2.
29. *The Bible as History,* by Werner Keller, 1964 edition, p. 161.
30. *Living With the Bible,* by Moshe Dayan, 1978, p. 39.
31. *The Sun,* San Bernardino, California, October 19, 1967, p. B-12.
32. *The Bible and Archæology,* by Frederic Kenyon, 1940, p. 279.
33. *Rivers of the Desert,* by Nelson Glueck, 1959, p. 31.

Chapter 18
The Bible—Is It Really Inspired by God?

1. *The Encyclopædia Britannica,* 1971, Vol. 22, p. 452.
2. *The World Book Encyclopedia,* 1984, Vol. 19, p. 445.
3. *Encyclopedia Americana,* 1977, Vol. 27, p. 331.
4. *Biblical Researches in Palestine,* by E. Robinson and E. Smith, 1856, Vol. II, p. 463.
5. *Great Books of the Western World,* edited by Robert Maynard Hutchins, 1952, Vol. 6, p. 43.
6. *Ibid.*
7. *Ibid.*
8. *Ancient Near Eastern Texts Relating to the Old Testament,* edited by James B. Pritchard, 1969, p. 316.
9. *Archaeology and Bible History,* by Joseph P. Free, 1962 revision, p. 284.
10. *The Works of Flavius Josephus,* Wars of the Jews, translated by William Whiston, 1874, Book II, chap. XIX, par. 7, p. 642.
11. *The Ecclesiastical History of Eusebius Pamphilus,* translated by Christian Frederick Cruse, August 1977, ninth printing, p. 86.
12. *Josephus,* Wars of the Jews, Book V, chap. XII, par. 3, p. 734.
13. *Josephus,* Wars of the Jews, Book VII, chap. I, par. 1, p. 762.
14. *Josephus,* Wars of the Jews, Book VI, chap. IX, par. 3, p. 760.
15. *The First World War,* by Richard Thoumin, quoting preface, 1964, p. 10.
16. *Der Spiegel,* No. 27, July 5, 1982, p. 119.
17. *The London Times,* "Malnutrition Now Afflicts a Thousand Million People," June 3, 1980, p. 10.
18. *The Globe and Mail,* Toronto, "The Vital Task of Finding Food for a World Already Reeling With Hunger," by A. Roy Megarry, November 8, 1983, p. 7.
19. *The Guardian,* London, "Millions Starve as Worldwide Disaster Hits," by Victoria Brittain, September 30, 1983, p. 10.
20. *Time,* "China's Killer Quake," June 25, 1979, p. 25.
21. *Il Piccolo,* October 8, 1978.
22. *Science Digest,* "1918: The Plague Year," by Joseph E. Persico, March 1977, p. 79.
23. *U.S.News & World Report,* "Terrorism: Old Menace in New Guise," interview with Walter Laqueur, May 22, 1978, p. 35.
24. *Die Welt,* January 18, 1979, p. 17.
25. *The West Parker,* Cleveland, Ohio, January 20, 1966, p. 1.
26. *The New York Times,* "Macmillan, at Yale, Reflects on Change," November 23, 1980, p. 51.
27. *1913: America Between Two Worlds,* by Alan Valentine, 1962, p. xiii.
28. *You Can Live Forever in Paradise on Earth,* published by the Watchtower Bible and Tract Society of New York, Inc., 1982, pp. 136-141.
29. *The World Magazine,* August 30, 1914.
30. *Of Guilt and Hope,* by Martin Niemöller, 1947, p. 48.

Picture Credits

Pictures listed in order of appearance on page

No, Living Forever Is Not Just a Dream

As you have seen from Chapter 19, Paradise is soon to come. The book *You Can Live Forever in Paradise on Earth* provides more information on how you can live forever in that Paradise.

The book also considers subjects about which many people have questions, such as what happens at death, how Armageddon makes way for the Paradise earth, who are to be resurrected and where, what Judgment Day is, and what you must do to live forever.

The book's 256 large-size pages are filled with over 150 teaching illustrations, most in beautiful color. Copies will be sent to you for $3.00 (U.S.) each, postpaid.

Also, you may send for the *New World Translation of the Holy Scriptures*, a Bible in modern English, for $4.00 (U.S.). It is bound in black vinyl and contains marginal references, an appendix, and a concordance. (Contributions subject to change)

Send to Watch Tower, using one of these addresses: